THE
INCARNATING
CHILD

Joan Salter

HAWTHORN PRESS

The Incarnating Child Copyright © 1987 Joan Salter

Published by Hawthorn Press, Hawthorn House, 1 Lansdown Lane, Stroud, Gloucestershire. GL5 1BJ, UK.
Tel: (01453) 757040 Fax: (01453) 751138
E-mail: info@hawthornpress.com Web site: **www.hawthornpress.com**

Typeset in Plantin by Southgate Solutions, Gloucestershire.

Printed in Great Britain, 1987
Reprinted 1994
Reprinted 1996
Reprinted 1999
Reprinted by The Bath Press, 2002

British Library Cataloguing in Publication Data
Salter, Joan
    The Incarnating Child – (Lifeways)
    1. Child rearing 2. Spiritual direction 3. Spiritual life
    I. Title II. Series
    291.4 4 BV1590

ISBN 1 869 890 04 3

Contents

Dedication

To the many charming Gabriel children and their parents.

> The mighty sun has warmed you
> You've come from cosmic spaces
> The stars have given soul life
> The Gods have worked upon you.
>
> Now your task is calling
> We welcome you to earth life
> Your destiny awaits you
> We ask God's blessing for you.

Introduction

When Joan Salter first wrote to me in the autumn of 1983, inviting me to give a number of lectures in Melbourne, I perceived her to be a person of initiative, with genuine will impulses. When we met in the spring of 1984 and I was hospitably received into Joan's home, I perceived a loving heart, a heart predestined to create a counselling centre for mothers. The Gabriel Baby Centre provides an example which one would like to see copied in every city in the world. During the days we spent together I was then able to gain closer understanding of the real nature of this remarkable woman who has now written this unique, inspired book which shows how the insights of Rudolf Steiner's spiritual science can be brought to realization in everyday life.

The path the spiritual soul takes towards incarnation on this earth is an initiation process. Severing its close bonds with the spiritual world, the soul sets out to find the way to a particular father and mother who will provide the physical basis for its developing body. Gabriel, the angel of the Annunciation, is the protective spirit watching over the child's progress from its development in the womb to birth and beyond, until school age is reached. This development, this process of incarnation, is very much under threat today through lack of understanding and lack of love, through stress and a onesided materialistic way of thinking that is no longer able to see the developing human being as a whole consisting of body, soul and spirit. It needs someone of the calibre of Joan Salter to spearhead efforts to undo all those wrongs.

It was more than ten years ago that Joan established the Gabriel Baby Centre, bringing great leadership qualities to the work: solid scientific foundations, years of work in spiritual science to penetrate the laws which govern the coming into being of a human individual, and years of practical nursing experience. This book presents the full fruit of a life devoted to helping and healing.

This is a book I feel I can endorse and recommend with all my heart. In daily medical practice I am only too often confronted with the consequences of disrupted, incomplete and inadequate incarnation processes. Many of my cancer patients were deprived of warmth in family life, of real maternal love, maternal understanding, during their growing years, and this has led to a feeling of isolation that has left deep imprints in the life history. Many of them were unwanted children growing up in homes lacking in harmony. All this can finally lead to a 'Cancer mentality' which precedes the physical manifestation of cancer by many years.

With cancer the most threatening of diseases in the present age, and with many other problems and diseases also due to present life styles, it is of the greatest importance that what this book has to say becomes widely known – not only to mothers-to-be but to families everywhere. If the author's suggestions are taken up, children will grow not only into healthier human beings but also into people of discernment and courage who take a genuine interest in their work and their fellow human beings and find a way of being creative in taking their place in social life.

Joan Salter has been able to present profound truths in this work in a way that can be understood and taken up in practice by anybody, whatever their educational background. For this, she deserves the gratitude of all mothers and the gratitude of future generations. With real respect, I should like to add my own gratitude for a truly social achievement.

Dr Rita Leroi
Medical Director
Lukas Klinik
CH 4144 Arlesheim
Switzerland

Foreword

This book presents the content of a study course on child care which I have conducted over the past ten years. The course is part of the work of the Gabriel Baby Centre,[1] and as such, presents a child care based on Rudolf Steiner's picture of man which he outlined earlier this century. (See Appendix A.) *Throughout the book the term 'man' indicates a member of humanity, and includes both male and female. Likewise the terms 'him', 'he' and 'his', include 'her', 'she' and 'hers'.* As the book will show, this knowledge of man can be applied to the most practical affairs, such as for example, choice of baby clothes, infant feeding, the right time for baby slings and so on. Yet, while in its application it is essentially practical, a true knowledge of the child carries one into lofty vistas of the spirit. It has been my purpose to encompass both these aspects, and this has necessitated a diversity of style. For a description of the spiritual demands its own style, and this must necessarily be different from a description of the mundane.

Throughout the book, I have been concerned to say something *new*. That seems the only valid reason for producing yet another book on child care. It is out of this concern that I have omitted much. For instance, I have not given lists of food for the expectant mother, not dealt with behavioural problems such as temper tantrums and sibling rivalry, nor have I mentioned potty training, teething troubles and all those other things so important for today's parents.

It is not that I regard these matters as unworthy of discussion – far from it! But so much has already been written about them, that another voice would scarcely be heard.

Other specific areas such as preparation classes for expectant parents, and the management of breast feeding, I have left to those more competent in these fields than I. Authorities such as Childbirth Education Associations, the Nursing Mothers Association of Australia, The Breast Feeding Support Group, U.K. and La Leche League, U.S.A. have a wealth of helpful material, support activities and scientific information readily available.

My aim, in a way, has been limited; yet, in another way, as wide as heaven itself. I have approached my subject from a spiritual-scientific[2] point of view. For, like many other areas of life today, the upbringing of the child has suffered, perhaps more than most, from a point of view which denies the spirit.

My task has been to present the spiritual reality of the child, and to outline a practical child care which recognises this. The attempt to do this has only been possible because of the body of knowledge given to the world by Rudolf Steiner.

Acknowledgements

I wish to thank:

Dr Rita Leroi, Medical Director, Lukas Klinik, Arlesheim, Switzerland – for generously writing an introduction.

Rob Gordon, Deputy Senior Psychologist, Royal Children's Hospital Melbourne – for directing me to sources of useful information.

Margaret Piper, Maternal and Child Welfare Nurse – for offering helpful suggestions related to infant care.

Adrian May, Member of the College of Teachers, Melbourne Rudolf Steiner School – for suggesting valuable additions to part of the text.

Rani Petherbridge, for making available her family's winter experience.

Joseph Mani, Musician – for supplying lullabies and songs for children.

Sue Schuster, Art Teacher – for her attractive drawings.

Wendy Duff and Jan Gauci, Kindergarten Directors – for collecting children's drawings for me.

Parents from the Gabriel Baby Centre, who have given me permission to use photographs of their babies, and their children's drawings.

Judy Halcombe, Secretary – for typing the manuscript.

Yvonne Morgan, Nurse – for helping with practical details.

Chapter One
Starting Point - Knowledge of Man

To bring up a child, to prepare him for adulthood, can only be successfully undertaken today if there is some basic knowledge of what an adult human being essentially is. We need a clear picture of our ultimate objective. This would seem an obvious first requirement, and must form the very foundation stone of our future discussion.

Our starting point, therefore, is to arrive at an understanding of the nature of man. Only then can we realistically proceed. Such an understanding can be gained largely by self-observation.

The Threefold Human Being ★

Let us observe ourselves. It is obvious that we have physical bodies perceptible to the senses. Of that we can be sure.

If we look a little more deeply, it is equally evident that we each have an inner life of likes and dislikes, impulses and urges, joys and sorrows. We can experience these as realities within us, although this inner life itself is not perceptible to the senses; one sees only its outer manifestation. Most people call this area of our being the psychological life. Psyche is a Greek word meaning soul, and it is this latter term which will be used throughout this book.

Yet, there is more to be observed. If I look carefully, I see that whether I am liking or disliking, whether I have an impulse to do this or an urge to do that, whether I am happy or sorrowful, throughout these soul fluctuations, I always experience myself as myself. I know I remain the same individual whatever changes there may be within me. Moods come and go, but throughout I remain my own individual self. This I experience also as a reality.

Consider, then, that the three-fold human being consists of an outer physical body, an inner life of soul, and an individual selfhood. *It is this whole that must be considered in bringing up a child;* it must be the basis right from the beginning . . . But this was not always so.

An Art of Parenthood, or a Science of Child-Rearing

In Great-Grandma's day things were different. A conscious knowledge of man as set out above was unnecessary for successful mothering. For Great-Grandma practised what could be described as an Art of Motherhood, and this arose within her instinctively. Out of herself she knew exactly what to do.

If there were a digestive upset she brewed a herbal potion; for inflammations she made a bran poultice. She acted with an instinctive surety, a confidence often sadly lacking today. And this was fine! Great-Grandma's art was adequate as long as things stayed within the norm.

But often there were abnormalities; and disease and infections struck. Then Great-Grandma was in real trouble for *she had no scientific knowledge to guide her*. At the beginning of this century there was an appallingly high infant mortality rate as gastro-enteritis and other allied diseases spread virtually uncontrolled.[1] Something more than instinct was clearly needed.

From this there arose a scientific approach to child care as doctors, nurses, and other professionals sought to stem the tide of epidemic. Many medical problems were solved, and the infant mortality rate dropped dramatically. It seemed as though the Science of Child-Rearing had all the answers. . . So it seemed!

But as parents adopted more and more this scientific approach, so in corresponding measure did the old instinctive art diminish. What was once an assured knowing became the subject of scientific debate. There was choice, and thus the possibility of error. This has led to a multitude of anxieties, as parents seek to 'do the right thing' and find their way amidst a vast literature on child care.

The Science of Child-Rearing has certainly solved medical problems, but it has not solved human problems. In fact, it has created and compounded them.

What, then, is to be done? To go back to Great-Grandma's day is neither possible nor desirable. We must ever go forward. Today we must develop a new art, an Art of Parenthood; and this must incorporate within it the scientific knowledge developed over the past decades.

This new art must be *consciously* practised. It cannot rely on instinct alone. Rather, must it have its basis in a conscious knowledge of the reality of the child.

Knowledge of man must indeed be the foundation stone of a new Art of Parenthood. That is the only valid basis for the present and the future.

* See Appendix B

Chapter Two
The Process of Incarnation

If our knowledge of man is to be adequate to our needs, it must include within it knowledge of the child's origin. This requires a science that is able to extend beyond the material – that is, a spiritual science.

The word 'incarnation' means entering into a body of flesh; and this process immediately poses questions. For example, who is it that enters this fleshly body, and from whence does the entering being come? These are crucial questions that need answers if we are to understand the child, and provide an appropriate home care at the practical level.

Our present day language, orientated to a technological society, is not adequate to answering these fundamental questions of life. It is the poets who illuminate such matters. They speak from a deeper level.

Wordsworth has much to say that is relevant –

> Our birth is but a sleep and a forgetting:
> The Soul that rises with us, our life's star
> Hath had elsewhere its setting,
> And cometh from afar:
> Not in entire forgetfulness
> And not in utter nakedness,
> But trailing clouds of glory do we come
> From God who is our home:
> Heaven lies about us in our infancy.[1]

The poet Eleanor Trives speaks in the same vein –

> Into my childhood days shone the loveliness
> Of the Kingdom before birth
> In a dream light that knew no death.
> Now at the end of my life
> Rays from the farther shore
> Reveal the immortality of all things mortal.[2]

The poets clearly indicate that the incarnating being is a human Soul/Spirit coming from a Kingdom or from God, and that during infancy there is an awareness of this 'heavenly' origin.

> There was a time when meadow, grove and stream,
> The earth, and every common sight,
> To me did seem
> Apparelled in celestial light. . .[3]

Wordsworth and Trives are not indulging in poetic fantasy, but what they say can be substantiated by spiritual science. In a series of lectures on 'The Study of Man', Rudolf Steiner had this to say: "Man descends, as it were, as Spirit-Soul or Soul-Spirit from a higher sphere into earthly existence. . . Physical existence here is a continuation of the spiritual."

It is difficult to find an adequate everyday terminology to indicate these areas of life, and in choosing terms one exposes oneself to misinterpretation and accusations of being totally unscientific. However, in spite of this, I have chosen to use Wordsworth's term 'heaven' to denote a non-material, non-spatial and non-temporal reality – a 'realm of being' rather than a place, from which the incarnating soul-spirit comes.

Thus it can be said – *the human spirit comes from heaven bringing a soul life with it.* ("Trailing clouds of glory do we come from God. . .") This is the reality of the incarnating child. The parents give a wonderful gift, a body, but do not create the essential being of the child. This human spirit already *is,* a living entity that enters the cell which will grow and provide the earthly body.

The process of incarnation must now be traced, and first we will turn to the scientists. It is a fascinating story.

In the 1920s a team of research embryologists in Vienna made an astounding discovery. They found that in the human being, the first fertilized cell does not grow into the baby, but develops into the so-called house of layers – that is, the chorion, amnion, allantois and yolk sac. Only at about the seventeenth day does the growth of the embryo actually begin.

After this, it takes another twenty-three days before the formation of body organs, kidneys, heart, etc., begins. That is, there is a period of forty days from fertilization until all the foundations of the body are laid down. We will take special note of this forty days. It is roughly six weeks. This procedure is quite different in animals. There, with the exception of certain apes, the first cell fertilized becomes the embryo. It simply increases in size and complexity until the form of the baby animal is produced. It could be said that the animal is born, but man incarnates.[4]

Obviously, man is related to the animals, yet he is no naked ape. He belongs to a different species altogether, to the family of man.[5] The human being, from the moment of fertilization onwards, has a different origin and different destiny from the animals. We will see this illustrated again later on. It is of the greatest significance.

At the beginning of this century, Rudolf Steiner, from his own spiritual-scientific research, found that the ego does not enter the body at fertilization, but 'waits' until the above mentioned sheaths are built. In 1906 he stated that the ego enters between the second and third week, that is, about the seventeenth day. At that time, the facts of the very early stages of embryonic growth were unknown. When they were discovered in the mid 1920s, it was found that they fully substantiated what Steiner had given twenty years earlier.

It is when the ego enters that many a mother-to-be has a vivid dream of a white bird or a shaft of light raying down upon her. She later discovers that she is pregnant. Other mothers report that they are aware of the child's presence hovering about them for some days prior to their dream. The incarnation of the Spirit (perhaps one could say, the annunciation) is not theory for these perceptive young women. It is a reality.

What are we to learn from these astonishing facts, and how can they be applied in a practical way to the care of the child?

Stanley Drake, in his book *Path to Birth* points out that, "in forty days, the incarnating being, who has previously lived free of time and space in the heavenly world, has achieved the first stage of adaption to existence in a world of space and time.

"So this period of forty days can be seen as a period of adjustment between spiritual and physical states."[6]

We thus recognise that forty days or six weeks is the time needed for the Spirit to adapt itself to new conditions.

It is interesting to note that in old myths, sagas and biblical lore, the period forty days is used to denote a significant change from one state of consciousness to another. From Genesis we learn that Noah spent forty days in the ark, and waited until the fortieth day to open the window. (See Appendix C.) Likewise, after the baptism in the Jordan, there was a forty day period of fasting in the wilderness of the desert.

Other examples could be given, but from what has already been said, it will be obvious that six weeks is a period demanding special attention. We must observe the baby carefully during the first six weeks of life, for here another adaption occurs. The baby comes from the watery realm into the realms of air and earth; and as well as physiological changes, there is a total change of consciousness. *The first six weeks of baby's life will call for very special care and understanding.*

Before discussing what this means in practical day-to-day caring, we must now turn to consider the mother's preparation during this wonderful progression of events.

It is a time for pondering deeply on the meaning of things as practical preparations are made.

Chapter Three
Preparation

Pregnancy has been with us since Adam and Eve. Yet it can never be common-place, for, as has been shown in the previous chapter, it involves a working together of heaven and earth. A human being has chosen to come, has joined with an earth body – surely a matter for great rejoicing, for careful preparation.

Pregnancy demands our attention from the beginning. Something special is happening, and this needs a special preparing. We must consider both body and soul. Outer and inner preparation must proceed hand-in-hand, but here we will first consider the former, and in the next chapter, the latter.

Body Preparation

Food: One of the most obvious ways for the expecting mother to prepare her body, is through the quality of her food. This means being concerned not only with its chemical composition – proteins, minerals, etc. – but with the very life of the food, with its living qualities and forces. (See Appendix D.)

Today, chemical pesticides, artificial fertilizers, and food additives such as colouring and preservatives all tend to destroy these life forces. Therefore, if possible, an expecting mother (and, indeed, all people) should try to obtain bio-dynamically grown produce, or, if this is unobtainable, then organically grown.

It is not proposed here to set out a recommended dietary regime, that aspect is well covered in today's literature. It is good quality food that must be strongly emphasized. This means grains, fruit and vegetables which carry maximum life forces, dairy products from cows that have grazed on bio-dynamically fertilized pastures (e.g. B.D. cheese and butter which are available from some health food shops), and eggs from hens that have run free and been fed organic food. Nuts, seeds and their cold pressed oils, and sprouted seeds add valuable vitamins and minerals to the diet. Whether one eats meat or not is a personal choice.

Dr Wilhelm Zur Linden in his book *A Child Is Born*, says "A high quality diet is not one which contains large amounts of meat, eggs and such like. What matters is that the food eaten should be as free as possible from chemical additives and other impurities." He adds that "Those who already have a varied diet of good quality food, need not change their ways when they become pregnant."[1]

Such good quality food is not easily obtainable, but there are some shops in which much can be found; and bio-dynamic gardeners' groups can give information.

It should be unnecessary to say that so called 'junk' food should be avoided throughout pregnancy. This also applies to alcohol, cigarettes and too much caffeine.

Diet is largely a matter of common sense, avoiding fanaticism on the one hand, and indulgence and carelessness on the other.

Herbs: Herbs have always been popular, and it is not surprising that many people today have a herb garden. During pregnancy herbs are particularly valuable, for they are full of health-giving qualities.[2]

The most important herb throughout the whole of pregnancy is the wild raspberry. Two or three cupfuls daily of raspberry leaf tea has a strengthening effect on the smooth muscles of the body, including the uterus. It is a must!

Dandelion is another excellent herb. It can be taken as tea using the leaf, or as 'coffee' made from the root. It is particularly helpful for morning sickness, especially if one is 'liverish'.

A herb rich in calcium, needed by both mother and baby is borage. The young leaves can be cooked or eaten raw, and the flower also can be eaten. Besides its calcium content, it is often a help for depression.

During the latter months, it is good to stock up with camomile, dill and fennel. They are all useful teas for a colicky baby, and camomile particularly has a calming effect both for mother and child. Much more could be said about these fascinating and health-giving herbs. They offer an endless and delightful journey of discovery.

More Body Care

The Perineum: Copper ointment and lime blossoms are particularly helpful to promote a good blood supply to and elasticity of the perineum. Dr Norbert Glas recommends that "during the last two months (of pregnancy) it is advisable to rub copper ointment into the perineal region, and during the ninth month a daily sitz (or hip) bath containing lime flower tea is recommended."[3] Zur Linden recommends that this should be taken only every second day, and adds, "stay in the bath for about ten minutes at first, but during the last two weeks for five minutes only."[4]

It is important that the water should be no hotter than 37°c. The bath is prepared by adding 600ml of boiling water to a handful of lime blossoms, covering, and allowing to infuse for five minutes. This is then strained and added to the bath water.

Stretch Marks: During pregnancy cold-pressed apricot oil or avocado can be used for massage to prevent stretch marks forming; or for treatment after birth should they occur.[5] The addition to the diet of seaweeds such as carrageen is also helpful as a preventative measure.

Nipples: Nipple care is a well recognized part of pregnancy preparation, and literature available through the Nursing Mothers' Groups gives much information.[6]

It is good to start preparation six to twelve weeks before baby is due. After the bath or shower gently pull the nipples out and roll them between thumb and forefinger. Then apply anhydrous lanolin, olive oil, or apricot oil, and very gently massage this into the nipples using a circular stroking action rather than a rubbing. At all costs avoid drying agents such as methylated spirits, for this is likely to lead to an eventual cracking of the nipple skin due to a drying effect on the skin's natural oils. It is important not to use talc powder, for this blocks the pores of the skin, whereas oils and lanoline are able to be absorbed. Nipple care is particularly helpful for blondes and 'red-heads' who usually have sensitive fair skin.

Relaxation: Relaxation classes conducted by Childbirth Education groups and maternity hospitals are also very much part of the pregnancy scene. There is no need for details here.

In all these ways can the expecting mother help the Great Mother Nature prepare her body. It will be of immense benefit to herself and to the well-being of the child.

Preparing Clothes for the Baby

Fabrics: The golden rule here is – use only natural fibres. Woollen and cotton garments are a must, and synthetics should be avoided. This poses a real challenge, for the majority of fabrics today are either totally or partially synthetic.

The skin is an important sense organ, separating our body from the environment, yet at the same time relating us to it through the senses of touch and temperature. The skin not only has a physiological function (e.g. sweating), but is also a vehicle for the expression of soul and spirit. We blush with embarrassment, go pale with fear and so on.

In the young child, especially an infant, the skin has a wonderful sensitivity, so much so that Ashley Montagu considers the sense of touch to be the most important of the senses during the first six months.[7] Therefore, the baby's clothes must be chosen with great care; they should be soft, warming, and have a caressing quality.

While speaking of the skin, it may be appropriate to mention the choice of baby soap, for this will be bought during the preparation period. The Swiss firm Weleda[8] makes an excellent product 'Kinderseife' (baby soap); and calendula soap is also good, for the marigold has healing and soothing properties.

But, to return to clothing –

Dr Otto Wolff,[9] in an article entitled 'Natural Versus Synthetics' published in Weleda News in 1980, has this to say: "He (man) can have no relationship to the synthetic products he takes in. These remain alien to his nature and are unable to evoke a direct response from his life forces, his soul or his spirit. Man, animal and plant have followed the same path of evolution and have a common foundation which is life. It is this life element which is lacking in all synthetic products. One might also describe synthetics as products not intended by nature." Dr Wolff is writing of natural and synthetic medicines, but the same principles apply to natural and synthetic fabrics.

The former give a sense of soul comfort, while the latter are alien to human nature. It can be observed how cold one often feels in synthetics (for example, acrylic), for the skin is unable to breathe properly and one tends to sweat.

Therefore, every effort should be made to obtain clothing made from natural fibres. The easiest and least expensive way to do this is to make the garments oneself! Knitting and sewing are to be recommended to the mother-to-be, for, as we will see later on, these activities have an effect on the soul as well as producing clothes for the baby.

Warmth: Warmth is essential for the young child. It will be dealt with again in Chapter Eleven. Suffice it to say now, that in a temperate climate it is essential for the baby up to one year of age to wear a woollen singlet virtually all the year round, except on very hot summer days.

During the first seven years of life, the ego is preparing the physical body to be the instrument through which the soul and spirit can function in later life. By the time the child is seven, he has a totally new body, for every cell has been changed. For this work to proceed with maximum efficiency, the body must be warm. It will be strange for some to hear that the ego works through the warmth organization of the body. But if one observes oneself when really cold, there is a noticeable 'cramping', and an inability to be fully oneself.

Therefore, it is most important for children up to seven years of age to be really warm, and this means wearing a pure woollen singlet on cool and cold days. These are obtainable in some shops; and for the home knitter it is important to buy pure wool, and not wool and synthetic mix.

It is good to provide some cotton singlets too. Babies with very fair skins and prone to rashes, are usually more comfortable with cotton next to the skin, and the woollen singlet on top.

Bonnets are out of fashion today, and many babies, even in winter time, have unprotected heads. In the first year, the brain grows as much as during all the rest of life. In fact it parallels the chest growth. For this amazing feat to be carried out efficiently, the head needs to be kept warm. Two or three woollen bonnets are a necessary addition to the list of clothes, for a lot of body heat is lost through an unprotected head.

Flannel pants (sometimes called 'pilchers') are highly recommended; and towelling or flannelette nappies are much to be preferred to disposables.

Colours: The choice of colours is another important area to consider. The traditional choice of pink or blue was founded on a knowledge of the 'being' or expression of the colour, not on a personal arbitrary preference. There is considerable literature on this subject which looks at the characteristics and gesture of the various colours.[10]

The best colours for the baby are rosy pink, mauve, pale blue, a sunny yellow or creamy white. Brown and green should be avoided, for they are too 'earthy' for the young child. We will see later on, that well into the pre-school years, the child's inner experiencing is more orientated to heaven than to earth. And this is almost totally so for the baby. Earthy colours have no place in the young child's inner experiences, and so are unsuitable for the early years. This also applies to grey and other drab colours. It is not incidental that Raphael gave his Madonnas a rose pink gown and blue cloak, and the Child a golden halo.

Rudolf Steiner has recommended that during the early weeks it is of immense value to the baby to live within a rose-pink-blue atmosphere. He suggests achieving this by the use of two silk veils, one blue and the other pink. These are placed one on top of the other over the crook of the bassinet and draped around the basket, leaving a space to ensure adequate ventilation. The light shining through these creates a mauve colour; and there is the added advantage of the sharp contours of the world being softened. This is particularly helpful for the baby in the first six weeks of life. Mothers who have used these veils report on the tranquillity of the child.

The pram needs to be chosen carefully, as many are lined with black. Those which are off-white inside are much to be preferred. Imagine the effect of black on an infant. It is the colour of mourning!

Colours for the bassinet lining, blankets (pure wool, of course!), bunny rug, cot cover etc. need also careful choosing. If someone gives you a 'horror' as a gift, have the courage not to use it! The well-being of the baby is the prime consideration.

We are all deeply affected by colour. The idiom of the language expresses it admirably. We 'see red', are 'in the pink', have 'the blues', or are in a 'black mood'. The young child is tremendously sensitive to the different nuances of colour, and will feel their effect deep within his soul.

"Colour speaks. Its universal language passes over all boundaries of race or nation . . . Children understand it and respond to it immediately.

Colour is to the soul almost as great a necessity as air is to the body."
Gladys Mayer[11]

Outer preparations are complete. It is time to look inward. Indeed, inward preparation has been going on all the time as the soul continuously attunes itself to the coming event.

Chapter Four
Anticipation

Having made preparation on the physical level, we must now turn our attention to the soul life. Here we find strong forces at work. Emotions manifest, there are the longings of pregnancy, and there is a wondrous anticipation as the months go by. It is a time for dreaming dreams, contemplating the Infinite, for being in tune with the universe.

Today, there is less opportunity for these deeper feelings to come to the surface. The mother-to-be often feels obliged to continue at work right up to the last month. There are financial obligations to be met – the mortgage on the house, payments on the car, and the cost of equipment for the baby. These are pressing demands which necessitate two incomes for as long as possible. The morning rush, evening tiredness, and the demands of the work situation all take their toll of subtle inner stirrings.

It was not so for previous generations. Then, the mother-to-be remained at home. There was knitting to be done, baby's clothes to stitch, blankets to embroider. Friends called to admire the layette, to enthuse over Grandma's hand-knitted shawl, to bring a gift, to share the growing anticipation.

This was much more than a time for collecting baby clothes; it was also a significant soul preparation. There was a stirring of emotions, a rejoicing with friends; and most of all, it orientated the expecting one to the idea and reality of motherhood. The soul was prepared to receive the child with confidence.

It is not suggested that an attempt should be made to recapture the mood of past generations. We must find a way suitable for present day expecting parents to deepen their soul experience.

It is during this period that women often notice a change in their feeling life. A tenderness hitherto not experienced can develop; or there can be feelings of uncertainty and anxiety in the early months followed by an increase in confidence and strength from about the seventh month onwards. Some young women report "an inner peace never known before."[1] It is good to be aware of these soul stirrings and consciously work with them. Negative feelings must be transformed, and positive feelings nurtured and fully experienced.

Setting aside a short time each day – say ten or fifteen minutes – to concentrate one's thoughts upon the coming child, can give a great deal. A vivid visualization of the baby, and at the same time a mood of reverence and gratitude for the miracle of incarnation activates strong soul forces that prepare the life of feeling for the coming event. One sits quietly, relaxed in body and calm in mind as one pictures the coming child.

During pregnancy an opportunity exists to understand areas of life that are often neglected during the demands of every day affairs. It is now that the soul is much more open to usually unexplored higher realms. Here, a verse is often a help, especially if one fills the soul with its content.

> Into my will
> Let there pour strength,
> Into my feeling
> Let there flow warmth,
> Into my thinking
> Let there shine light,
> That I may nurture this child
> With enlightened purpose,
> Caring with heart's love
> And bringing wisdom
> Into all things.

Such a verse can be worked through by first entering into each line, and then filling the soul with the totality so that one lives fully into the whole content. This should not be a 'drifting away', but a fully conscious activity. To practise it consciously each day can have far-reaching consequences, not only during pregnancy but also for the whole of life. For such concentrated inner activity generates strengths and qualities of soul that are enduring and of timeless value.

Throughout the expecting months, the Raphael Madonnas are particularly helpful, and especially the Sistine Madonna. The latter is a truly heavenly picture. It portrays the archetypal Mother standing on the clouds of heaven, holding the heavenly child and surrounded by angelic faces. The other figures bring a mood of reverence. It is significant that the child is held upright. This shows the true posture of man. To make this picture the focus of one's thoughts and feelings is of immense value.

There are other matters to be reflected upon too. There is the child's destiny to be considered, the finding of a name, and baptism. How such matters are approached will depend very largely upon the parents' cultural background and philosophical or religious convictions. For example, destiny involves the idea of the child bringing with him certain pre-dispositions and aptitudes, of his seeking certain tasks in life, of relationships to be resolved and formed. Pregnancy is a good time to reflect upon these things.

Baptism and naming belong together. If it is the parents' intention to have the child baptised, thoughts and feelings can be prepared for this special sacrament. Prior discussion with Priest or Minister can be helpful in coming to an understanding of its meaning. This should also involve the godparents, for their task is essentially a spiritual one. They are charged with watching over the child's soul development and spiritual well-being. Baptism should not be done out of tradition, but from a conviction in the heart of the parents that it is a first step in the child's spiritual nurture.

Choosing a name is an individual matter. Fortunate is the man or woman who feels that his or her name is 'just right.' If parents are able to sense the child's true being either during pregnancy or immediately at birth, they often know the right name. Then, not only will the name suit the child, but the child and adult will suit the name. We may reflect upon the idea that our name is not only earthly but is 'written in heaven.'[2]

Finally, it is of great value for the mother-to-be to become orientated to home life for several months before the child's birth. This means giving up work and making the home the focus of activities for some considerable time beforehand. If this is achieved, the transition from career-girl to motherhood will be much easier. For, once the baby is born, the child in the home becomes one's focus; home life becomes a reality. If this has already been established, feelings of isolation and so on will be greatly minimised, or better still, non-existent.

In all these ways much can be done today. Enthusiasm, anticipation, reverence and gratitude are potent forces which prepare the soul for parenthood; and this is of immense value to parents and child alike. Anxieties and depression, feelings of not being able to cope, of being left out, are all too frequently part of today's experiences in the early weeks. The preparation of the soul as outlined above is a sure way to minimise or totally avoid these negative feelings.

For today's expecting parents, soul preparation is a must.

Chapter Five
The Phenomenon of Motherhood

An Interlude

A human being has incarnated! Preparations have been made, and the mother's body is ready to labour effortlessly.

It is the moment of birth. The head has crowned. There is a stillness and an atmosphere of quiet; voices are low, lights are dimmed, hearts are prepared to welcome a new being. A final triumphant push and the child is born. Labour is over; the miracle is accomplished.

It is a jubilant moment, experienced by Mother as the final act of initiation. A new stage of her life has begun, a new magic fulfilment is in process.

The baby is on her body, skin to skin, seeking the breast, nuzzling in, suckling. Bonding has commenced, communication is established.

Thus for many women today does motherhood begin – and it is a wonderful beginning. Father is there too, of course, and has contributed much; he also has caressed the child, and, like Mother, has gazed in wonderment at this new being.

But most truly it is Mother's moment, her agony and ecstasy. So, before going on, let us pause here for a while, and consider only Mother. Let us look carefully at this phenomenon of motherhood and see if it will reveal its secrets to us.[1]

We may well ask "what does motherhood offer a woman today? Is it worth all the effort involved?" If understood aright, it will be seen to offer a great deal that is new and specifically related to our times.

We meet the phenomenon of motherhood in the animal and human kingdoms. In the animal there is an instinctive tenderness and caring that expresses itself, for example, in the mother hen tucking the chicks under her wing, the mother cat washing the kittens by licking, etc. For an animal not to care for her young is an aberration, contrary to Nature.

Down the ages it has been largely this instinctive mother love that has guided and sustained human mothers. As we have seen, it expressed itself as an art of motherhood, and as such was adequate to the demands of its times. In unsophisticated communities it is this instinctive mothering that still guides women; and indeed, often in developed western communities, some mothers still act more out of instinct than a consciousness suitable for our day. But this is rapidly changing.

Because this instinctive art has given way more and more to a science of child rearing, and because what was formerly a natural confident undertaking is now often fraught with uncertainty, a sort of chaos has pervaded motherhood.

What are we to think of this? Has it any meaning and purpose? Does it offer the mother anything? Is there something new emerging from the chaos today?

Never has motherhood meant such a demand on the total being of a young woman as it does today. Formerly, even earlier this century, there was always a nurse-maid or an extended family to help and support. Today, young mothers experience an intense aloneness not known before. Added to this, there are the sleepless nights, the never-ending washing, housework, shopping, often a crying colicky baby and so on. Amongst all the joys of motherhood there are the 'Trials', and these are experienced with great intensity.

In the olden days, those seeking initiation went through the so-called 'Trials of the Temple'; and these Trials, if successfully surmounted, led to initiation, a gaining of spiritual wisdom, a growth of the Self.

The seeker of our time does not enter an Initiation Temple, but rather, seeks within what could be called 'The Temple of Life'. Within this, as it manifests today, there are many paths of self development. Motherhood is one of these.

Mothers tread this path as they attempt to meet all the demands of present-day family life. There is often a sense of loss of identity. "I seem to be only 'Mum' not really me" is a fairly common comment. It is a shedding of old values, the former bright social or business life, and a gaining of new insights much more meaningful, more challenging.

Here there are new possibilities. Indeed, it can be said that motherhood today offers the possibility of initiation within the Temple of Life.

But there is something more. There is the timeless image of the Woman and Child as it has been known down the ages.

What does this image present to us? Is it relevant for our time?

From the most ancient times, people of different cultures have spoken in different ways of this Mother principle. In our Christian tradition we speak of the Virgin Mary; there is Isis of the Egyptians; the Druids spoke of the Goddess Ceridwen, the Virgin of Light; there is the Earth Mother of the Greeks, Demeter; the Goddess Artemis of the Ephesians, and Diana of the Romans. These are different forms of the one eternal Virgin Being, the Archetypal Feminine.

In the human being, the Mother principle is the soul (she); and as the consciousness of the human soul changed over the ages, so did the Mother principle reveal herself in these different forms. In the Virgin Mary, this revelation reached its fullest and most exalted manifestation. We see it enshrined for us by Raphael in his 'Sistine Madonna'.

This Divine Feminine principle is most fully represented on earth in the mother and child. Thus today does motherhood give the possibility of revealing the Divine in its archetypal feminine form. It could be said that a true and conscious art of motherhood as it is practised by an increasing number of young women, gives an opportunity for the Divine Mother Being to work into human souls on earth, to be manifested amongst us.

Thus is motherhood a high exalted task, one connected with the deepest and most profound issues of life. It is this which many young mothers today sense so strongly and which sustains them in their daily life.

> "Mother and child – their archetype
> is the Madonna – belong together
> as a unity. This is a spiritual
> reality . . . "
>
> Norbert Glas[2]

Chapter Six
The First Six Weeks

Let us return to the new-born baby, and start by considering the first six weeks; that is, the first forty days after birth. Another transition has taken place. As noted in Chapter Two, the baby has come from the water element of the uterus to the air and earth elements of the world. This calls for a period of adjustment. The child must be given opportunity to adapt to the new conditions. Exposure to the world's rush and bustle must be avoided.

Therefore, one of the most important needs during the first six weeks, is a protective environment.

An old intuitive wisdom knew this, and in some cultures, after birth, mother and child were shielded from intrusion for the first six weeks by placing a small leafy branch over the front door. Friends and neighbours knew that this meant 'no disturbances please'.[1]

In our modern life, with all its demands, how can this be achieved?

The Protective Environment

During these early weeks, the baby should be kept indoors as much as possible in a well-ventilated and warm room. The blue and pink veils mentioned in Chapter Three should be placed one on top of the other over the crook of the bassinet and draped over the basket, making sure there is adequate ventilation. As already noted, the mauve-pink colour breaks the world's sharp contours and has a soothing effect on the child.

Trips in the car, bus or tram should be as few as possible (ask Father to do the weekend shopping!); the noise, rush and bustle of supermarkets, busy shopping streets, traffic, and large gatherings of people should be avoided at all costs.

The noise of the Hoover, blender, washing machine and similar household appliances is far too disturbing, and the worst offender is television. Mechanical sounds such as radio and taped music are better avoided in the early weeks and months. The best music for this age is a softly played lyre or flute;[2] and lullabies, sung by mothers and grandmothers down the ages, have a timeless value. We include some in the Appendices. (See Appendix E.)

This protective environment should not mean that Mother feels 'glued to the house'. But it does mean that busy noisy places and household disturbances should be avoided if possible. Sometimes a kindly friend or relative can be a saving grace, and allow Mother to have an hour or so to herself. At times, that is necessary!

Wrapping

During pregnancy the baby has been wrapped in the protective sheaths of amnion and chorion, and after birth needs a continuation of this experience by being securely wrapped in a bunny rug. To merely place the bunny rug over the baby and tuck it around is not enough during this very special time. Even on a hot day, a baby under six weeks, and in fact, throughout the early months should be dressed in a cotton singlet, nappie and light gown, and be loosely wrapped. On no account should the infant wear a nappie only and be left unwrapped. A piece of old sheeting is an ideal substitute for the bunny rug on these hot weather occasions.

Ashley Montagu substantiates this view. He speaks of "the newborn's great need for enfoldment . . . " and the need to be "covered from all sides . . . and only gradually be introduced to the world of more open spaces."[3]

Therefore, it can be said that *wrapping securely is essential in the early weeks.*

It is important to leave the arms free to point upwards. We will see that this is a typical infant gesture. To achieve this, place the baby diagonally across the rug, folding over each side in turn, and then folding the bottom up around the baby to make an extra layer.

Later on the child will want to feel freer, and then the bunny rug as well as the blanket can be placed over the baby and tucked in. The baby's body gestures will indicate the right time for this. There is much to be learned by observing these gestures carefully. We will look at them in Chapter Seven.

Bathing

During the first six weeks a daily bath is unnecessary and disturbing.

In winter and cool weather, bathing once a week is adequate, and during summer, twice a week. Only during heat-wave conditions should the infant be bathed more frequently. A daily sponge, keeping

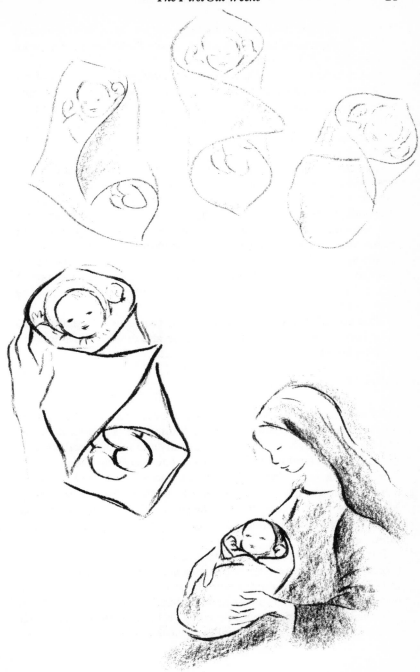

the baby covered as much as possible during the washing process, meets all hygienic needs. Towels and clothes should be warmed prior to starting, and the room should be warm.

Many babies vigorously protest, and obviously are afraid of the bathing ritual at this early age. Certainly there are some who, right from the beginning seem to find it relaxing, but even these are better left undisturbed until older. Except in the very hottest weather, three or four months of age is time enough for a daily bath. Then, all babies really enjoy it.

An exception to this general principle is the unsettled restless baby who wakes frequently at night. These little ones are sometimes calmed by a camomile bath before being settled down for the night. The bath can be prepared by making a family sized teapot of camomile tea, allowing it to infuse for a few minutes, then straining it into the bath water. Immerse the baby in the camomile water for four or five minutes then dry on a warmed towel. Follow with a little gentle massage, dress in warmed clothes, wrap securely and tuck into bed. A gentle lullaby accompanied on the lyre brings a further calming atmosphere.

This doesn't work for all babies, but frequently is found to be a great help, especially if Mother feels calm and relaxed while doing it. Bathing should not be done just after a feed.

Baby Massage

Baby massage has become popular since the recognition that it is one way of meeting the child's need for comforting tactile experiences, and because of its help for the restless baby or one distressed by colic. Often, a gentle stroking rather than a real massage is all that is needed. Amelia Auckett recommends it also for sudden or difficult weaning, difficulty in getting on to the breast, teething and constipation.[4] Massage works not only through the sense of touch but also through the body's warmth organization, hence its capacity to comfort, and often heal.[5]

For the young infant whom we are considering, it is best to think in terms of a gentle caressing rather than a 'massage session'. Sensitive mothers will do this quite naturally when bathing or washing the baby, changing the nappie or just cuddling. To disturb an infant by arbitrarily undressing him for his massage, or taking him to a massage session during these very special early weeks, is of no benefit to him.

Caressing, cuddling, and breast feeding at home will adequately meet all his early tactile needs.

Baby Slings

Should the very young child be carried for long periods in an upright baby sling?

It was Jean Liedloff's book, *The Continuum Concept* which popularized her idea that the baby needs to be in constant contact with the mother's body from birth until the commencement of crawling. This is based on a number of false premises and for the modern 20th Century mother is thoroughly impractical. (See Appendix F.)

An upright sling is a real help for the baby with colic, for the warmth of Mother's or Dad's body and the vertical position is often the only means of comfort. But the child does not need to be constantly carried, and in fact, if we observe the child we will see that *the natural position for the baby in the first six weeks is the horizontal.*

For those who wish to carry baby in the early weeks, a 'rebozo' is much to be preferred to an upright sling. This is a long woven cotton or woollen shawl used by generations of Mexican mothers to carry their infants. It allows the baby to remain in the horizontal. Directions on how to make and tie the shawl are given in Appendix G by kind permission of the Nursing Mothers' Association of Australia. (See Appendix G.)

During this time, when, hopefully, the infant is sleeping most of the day, the ideal place is his bassinet or cradle covered with the veils previously mentioned, and a quiet room. Later, a sheltered spot in the garden is also ideal.

At about three to four months when the child is making an effort himself to be upright, a sling for short periods is often a convenience and a pleasurable experience for parent and child – for example, going for a walk, or being out in the garden together.

Weighing

If everything is going well, mother confident *and there are no problems,* an early visit to the Infant Welfare Centre for weighing and checking is of no benefit to the baby. In almost all cases, three weeks is early enough for the first visit even for a first baby, and for subsequent children, when Mother has more confidence in her own judgement, and the child is obviously thriving, she may wish to wait a week or two longer.

The little one will have been thoroughly checked by the doctor at birth, and probaby rechecked by a trained nurse before discharge from hospital; and if the birth were at home, a midwife or district nurse will have been attending. Added to this, parents are usually the first to detect anything wrong with their child. If Mother is anxious, a request for a home visit will enable discussion without disturbing the infant.

Over the last few decades, baby's weight gains have been grossly over emphasized as a criterion of well-being. It is probably a hang-over from the bad old days when many children died from undernourishment or debilitating illness such as gastro-enteritis. Then regular weight gains were essential, as of course they are today in certain conditions – for example, premature babies. *But if the infant is obviously thriving, weekly weighing is not necessary even in the early months.* In fact, it tends to undermine the mother's confidence in her own mothering skills.

A further comment here is that the well-being of the baby is the paramount thing, not the weight as such. Therefore, the infant should have his singlet left on and be wrapped in a nappie (warmed if possible) for weighing. It is easy enough to deduct the weight of these afterwards. For a very young baby to be put naked on the scales each week may be more accurate statistically, but it is certainly not more accurate from the point of view of the child's real needs.

At Six Weeks

The baby has reached six weeks of age, and like Noah at the forty days, is ready to open a window on the world. Parents now notice a change. The child is becoming more alert, is smiling and communicating, and seems more aware of the surrounding environment. Slowly, the journey towards earth consciousness is beginning.

Now he is ready to enter more into family life. He will be accustomed to ordinary household noises, the sounds of older children romping and playing, people's voices, people walking about in his room, visitors, and normal family activities. If mother wishes to have some gentle music on the radio occasionally and the sounds waft over to his room, he will now adjust more readily to it. But television and the mechanical sounds mentioned previously should be avoided, and it is best not to have him near the radio or expose him to it for long periods. We will discuss the tremendous importance of good quality sense impressions in Chapter Eleven. However, once the infant has 'opened a window on the world', he will certainly enjoy a greater participation in things going on around him.

This is the time to introduce him to the family garden. He will be fascinated by the breeze moving leaves of trees, seeing birds hop or fly about and so on. He has now outgrown the silk veils, and a net can be tucked around the bassinet or pram. (A pram should have the hood partially folded back so the child, when awake, can see what's going on). A protected spot in mottled sunshine is ideal for cool days, and a shady place is best for really warm weather. Head and eyes should be protected from the sun and a bonnet is essential. Of course, he needs to be warm enough.

A well-loved garden is much more than merely a collection of plants. It has an atmosphere which speaks to the child, and often a restless baby will be calmed by being out of doors in such a place. To sleep in the garden for an hour or so, or just be there watching and listening, absorbing what Wise Mother Nature has to offer, is a helpful and healthy experience for a child from about two months of age onwards.

For those who live in an upstairs flat, a walk in the park once or twice a day is the next best thing.

New Vistas Ahead

We have been considering the importance of a protective environment during the early weeks. It will be seen that this calls for commonsense and a perception of and sensitivity to the needs of the human spirit at the very beginning of its earth pilgrimage. Many young parents today have these qualities. Their children are greatly blessed and will have the best possible start in life.

We must now proceed to the next stage. The baby is rapidly acquiring new skills which call for understanding. How to proceed will be our next concern. The child himself will point the way. Let us observe his body gestures.

Chapter Seven
The Baby's Body Gestures

An imaginative observation of the baby's body gestures reveals that the child's development recapitulates stages of the evolutionary process. He "presents a Little World of microcosm over against the macrocosm."[1] As we will see, this can be traced through vast ages of geological time. We start in the ancient Palaeozoic era of plants through the Mesozoic to the Tertiary.[2] The child, as he unfolds is a mirror of vast cosmic processes.[3] His gestures not only reveal these, but they speak to us of what is required at each stage.

Throughout the first year the baby strives after the vertical, ever seeking to achieve the true human gesture of uprightness. It is a clear indication, as stated in Chapter Two, that while the human being is related to the animal, one is able to observe something more in the human child. The kitten and foal are ever satisfied with the horizontal – there is no such striving to be upright.

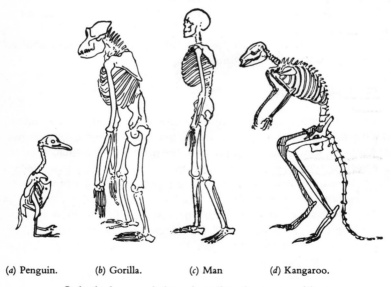

(*a*) Penguin.   (*b*) Gorilla.   (*c*) Man   (*d*) Kangaroo.

Only the human skeleton has taken the erect position.
From *Man and Animal* by Hermann Poppelbaum.

In his book *Man and Animal* Hermann Poppelbaum elaborates this with convincing clarity. He describes man's form and shape – hand, brain, foot etc., and compares these with the animal. He goes on to state "Man wrests his upper body free from the force of gravity." It is an awe-inspiring gesture. No wonder parents are elated when their child takes his first step.

The figure opposite shows that even the gorilla and kangaroo do not stand upright. They have failed to reach the stature of man.

But let us start from the beginning, for then we shall see how, during the first year, the ego gradually brings the body under its control until its human stature is attained. We have seen how the ego incarnates into the embryo at about the seventeenth day; that is, it has been there almost from the beginning. Now, after birth, it must incarnate into every part of the body, preparing its habitation for future use. This gradual process can be clearly seen by the discerning observer. Accompanying this ego penetration of the body, is a gradual awakening of consciousness.

Plant Gesture

The infant during the first six weeks of life is only dimly conscious of his worldly surroundings, and certainly has no consciousness of himself as an individual. As far as he knows, he could be Tom, Martha or anyone else. To come to clarity of himself as an individual will take the ensuing three years. At this stage, he is totally asleep in consciousness of self. In so far as this is so, it can be said that he has a plant-like consciousness. For the geranium also has no feeling of its 'geranium-ness'. Looking at the sleeping child in this imaginative way one sees in the raised arms a plant-like gesture. We are at an early Palaeozoic Age.

Just as the young plant coming up from seed raises its two first leaves, the cotyledons, so does Phoebe point her arms upwards. All healthy children make this gesture; and just as the leaves of a wilting plant droop, so do the arms of a really sick infant tend to droop downwards.

The new infant needs to live fully within this 'asleep' state of consciousness. Yet, many modern child care practices, designed to stimulate the child from the very earliest weeks, deny the infant this experience. For example, we are told "You should begin by filling your infant's life with sensory stimuli and motor activity the first week

Plant gesture – Phoebe at 1 week

you bring him home from the hospital."[4] One may well ask "What long-term effect is this likely to have?" It is well known that children denied the crawling stage often have learning difficulties at school. It therefore seems that to miss a stage has far-reaching harmful consequences. A child in the early weeks is probably at the most vulnerable stage of his life. Surely, to be denied the plant-like experience can only be harmful.

The practices outlined in the previous chapter give opportunity for the plant-like consciousness to be maintained over the early weeks. The gesture speaks of the need for protection; and just as the young seedling needs special nurture and protection before being planted out, so it is with the new born baby.

Fish Gesture

A later Palaeozoic period, the Silurian, saw the development of fishes, and a little later (geologically speaking!) the amphibians appeared. Prior to this, there was the watery plant life of seaweeds. It is not surprising to find, therefore, that the next gesture made by the child is reminiscent of the fish.

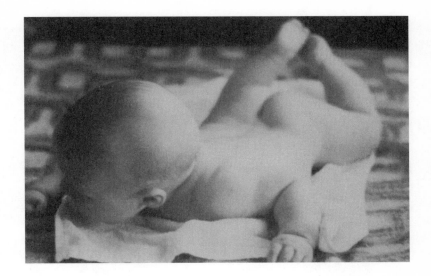

Fish gesture – Simon at 3 months

Simon at 3 months is still very much in the horizontal. He attempts to raise his head when in the prone position but is unable to maintain it; he relapses again to the horizontal. His legs are not extended, but he bends them up to resemble a fish's tail; and the arms at his side are like fins. He wriggles, often swishes his legs about, and makes swimming movements with his arms. These movements are well recognized by authorities on child development.[5] This fish gesture extends from approximately two to four months. The time and duration of its manifestation varies greatly with each individual child – as indeed, do all the gestures.

Here, there is a greater alertness than earlier, an obvious striving to maintain the head above the horizontal, and much more movement in the limbs. It is at about three months that the baby discovers his hands, and begins to move his arms with purpose. He is also able to clasp and unclasp his hands. The ego is learning to control and use the arms, and will soon be able to grasp objects.

The fish gesture calls for opportunity to move the limbs and wriggle about when awake. This is the time for the bunny rug sometimes to be placed over the baby during waking times to allow greater freedom. The firm wrapping of the earlier weeks can be modified for daytime,

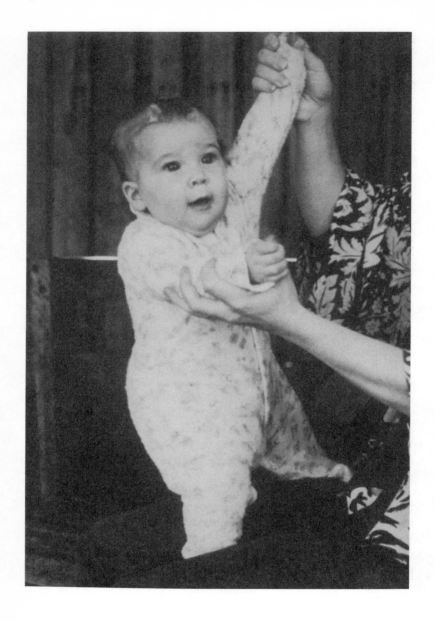

Mirabai – upright, at 4 months

but it is still good to wrap firmly for the night's sleep especially during the winter. About four months is the time for rattles (there are some good wooden ones obtainable) and from three to four months onwards the baby will be fascinated by a mobile.

Some parents notice that during this period, the baby makes frog-like swimming movements while in the bath. He has reached the amphibian stage!

But look at Mirabai! Here there is no fish or frog. Here speaks the supremacy of the human spirit as it holds the body aloft striving to overcome the limitations of what has gone before.

But patience, Mirabai! Your body must proceed on its destined way. There are other stages, more challenges ahead . . . But we will note your gesture and all that it implies – and it can be put to good practical use as well.

Mirabai's gesture is typical of a child of about three months and onwards.[6] There is a strong urge to be upright; and in this we find the answer to the right time for upright baby slings!

From this stage onwards, babies tend more and more to follow their own individual pattern. Some now go on to a bird gesture ('flying'), and follow this by crawling (mammalian gesture); while others miss the bird stage, and go from fish to reptile to mammal.

Bird gesture – Gabrielle 4½ months

Bird Gesture

At four months Gabrielle started 'flying'. It marked our discovery of the bird gesture!

Later, James confirmed that here, indeed, was the bird stage. The great Palaeozoic Era which includes the Silurian period has advanced to the Mesozoic. We are at the Triassic geological period.

It will be seen that now the baby's arms have become wings, and legs kick up in the air as if in flight. The child seems hardly attached to the earth. It is a time of increased mobility. The gesture speaks of the need for free movement, and this is the right time to put the child on the floor to kick and 'fly'. Even if a child does not make this gesture (and it is not a common one) babies of about four months and onwards need opportunity for this experience of freedom. Soon the baby will be rolling over and needs space on the floor to practise this. It is the time to think of safety: the child should never be left unattended on a table or near stairs.

As stated above, many children (probably most) develop from the fish stage to the reptilian. The lizard and the snakes emerge as the child becomes a 'land creature'. But it must be emphasized again that in all these gestures there are wide variations in time and in the actual gesture itself.

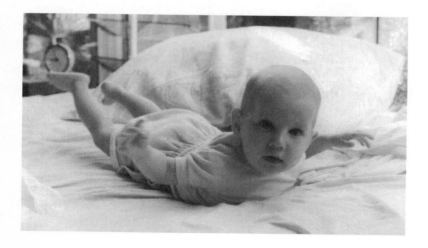

Bird gesture – James 5 months

Reptile Gesture

One momentous day, when her son was about seven months, Cheryl telephoned the Gabriel Baby Centre. She was obviously excited. "Emrys is a goanna", she said. There was an immediate understanding of what she meant, for a week or two previously we had been discussing the baby's body gestures. Unfortunately there is no photograph to record this historic moment. Yet it is not unsung in the annals of the Gabriel Centre, for it marked an important discovery – Emrys had proceeded from the Silurian to the late Carboniferous or early Permian period. He was at the stage of the lizards.

Cheryl had grown up on the land and was very familiar with the typical goanna gesture. The creature, lying on the ground is sensitive to the slightest sound; it swings its head around to any slight noise. This is what Emrys had done when his mother had tip-toed into the room. Then, goanna-like he had scuttled away, not yet crawling, but with a snake-like action of pulling himself along the floor. In all his movements he portrayed the family of reptiles.

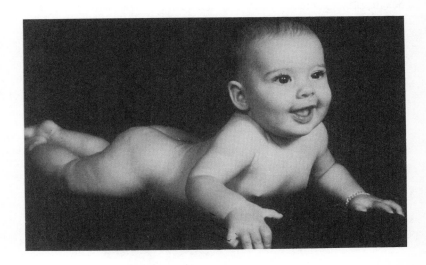

Reptile gesture – Ellise at 7 months

The picture of Ellise shows this stage. It will be noted that the head is well controlled, and chest and head are maintained above the horizontal (both the lizard and the snake are capable of rearing up the front part of their body.) The ego, which has already brought the head and arms under its control, is now working on the body.[7] The process of incarnation is proceeding. The legs, unlike the fish stage, are now fully extended resembling a lizard's tail, and the fins have become lizard's front feet. The child's snake-like movements on its belly further confirm the reptile gesture. It is a creeping, not a crawling.

Here we see a need for space and freedom. The child's obvious delight in his new-found mobility highlights its significance. Yet, it is at this stage that children are frequently put into walkers. It is a dreadful insult to burgeoning independence and the activity of strong will forces. Its effects will be harmful and far-reaching to both body posture and soul.[8]

If parents have misguidedly used a walker, there is a good deal that can be done to partially compensate for its harmful effects. These children, at whatever age, need opportunity for free movement. The young child can be encouraged to run, climb, jump and play active games. For older children, swimming is ideal, running along the beach, playing 'chasey', skipping and so on. It is the sense of freedom and body activity that must be recaptured.

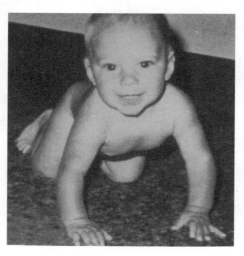

Quadruped gesture – John at 8½ months

Quadruped Gesture

The lower mammals bring us to the Jurassic period, and the quadrupeds to the following Cretaceous period. Crawling obviously belongs to the latter, for, as John shows, the child is up on all fours.

Like the preceding stage, the gesture demands freedom and space. Here there develops a real sense of body freedom. This is an important foundation stone, for in later life there is the possibility for it to metamorphose into a sense of inner soul freedom. To experience in infancy a sense of body freedom gives the opportunity for an adult capacity to 'flow out' freely into life in an uninhibited way, to be able to overcome restrictions at all levels. According to Norbert Glas, "This sense (of movement) has great importance for the human soul. Through it we come to feel free beings."[9]

To be restricted in a walker is even more harmful at this stage than previously. The child is denied this opportunity to lay a foundation for his future feeling of freedom. Play-pens, unwisely used, are also harmful for the same reason; although a short period in the playpen to enable Mother, for instance, to have a shower or telephone conversation knowing her adventurer is safe, is a legitimate use. It is a matter of common sense and parental sensitivity.

Human Gesture

Finally in this long drama, we come to the late Tertiary period. The body, in its gestures has recapitulated all the previous stages. As we have seen, the human spirit has been active all the way through, urging the body on to the next stage, knowing it must reach its consummation in the vertical. Only then, will it be a fitting habitation for the being man.[10]

Hayden achieved this at ten and a half months, but the period extends from approximately nine to fifteen months. The gesture asks for opportunity to explore, to investigate, to learn about the world. The toddler is primarily an adventurer, seeking out into new areas of experience. Kitchen cupboards, pot plants, power points, knobs, holes, flowers, father's tools and, in fact, everything has to be investigated. It calls for patience on the part of parents, and also guidance. The house must be made safe and limits must be set. Some things are obviously out of bounds.

It demands the loving heart of a saint, and the wisdom of Solomon.

Human gesture – Hayden at 10½ months

Fortunately for the toddler, many parents have these qualities.

This is the time for long-handled carts to push, balls to chase, for all things that move. A basket of waste materials will be explored with interest – gum nuts, acorns, smooth stones, cotton reels, wood off-cuts, small blocks and so on. They need to be big enough so they can't be swallowed. Again, safety, including safe playthings, is a major item at this stage.

Microcosm and Macrocosm

It has been shown that the human spirit was there from the beginning; it incarnated on the seventeenth day after conception.

This points to a tremendously significant fact, one which completely refutes the theory of a man's animal origin.

Again it shows in microcosm what Steiner found to be a truth – namely, that in the development of our cosmos the human spirit was there from the beginning; man was the primal creation.[11] He was nurtured in the bosom of the Gods (as the embryo is nurtured in the uterus), and his appearance on earth had to wait until the form appropriate to his spirit-being had been created.

To watch the child unfold through this great evolutionary panorama, seeing the ego express itself by pulling the body upwards, defying the law of gravity as the blood flows upwards to the head, is to be filled with humility and wonder. For here in the child, we most truly witness the handwork of the Gods.

Chapter Eight
Body Gestures and the Days of Creation

For those who are adventurous in thought and daring in vision, the baby's body gestures outlined in the previous chapter can be related to what is portrayed in imagery in the first chapter of Genesis – the Days of Creation.

So, ignoring the risk of being considered 'beyond the pale', let us with assured tread explore the realms to which this idea leads.

We are told that "In the beginning God created the heaven and the earth. And the earth was without form, and void; and darkness was upon the face of the deep . . . " Could this be a portrayal of conception and the days immediately following? There is certainly not yet a 'form', and the uterus at that stage is 'void' for fertilization takes place in the fallopian tube.

We then learn that "the spirit of God moved on the face of the waters." It is well known to those familiar with this process that the fertilized ovum reaches the uterus as a tiny 'seed' enclosed in a watery sphere of cells – a vesicle. This digs its way down into the uterine lining, the outer cells multiplying rapidly and penetrating a number of blood vessels. This enables a free flowing of blood to the implanted seed which in a few weeks will be a recognisable embryo. Here we have a picture of a very early watery stage.

Now comes the seventeenth day, when the spirit 'moves into' this watery mass. And at that moment God said "Let there be light and there was light." Thus is portrayed the First Day.

The Second Day brings the development of a "firmament in the midst of the waters," and eventually the waters divide. The unformed embryo has now become a foetus, and floats in the amniotic fluid, a veritable "firmament in the midst of the waters." Later on, just as labour is beginning, there is the breaking of the waters. The amniotic fluid 'divides' itself from the foetus and flows out down the birth canal. The baby is born and becomes physically divided from the mother. In these processes, the Second Day becomes visible.

On the Third Day we see the young infant's plant gesture. "And God said, Let the earth bring forth grass, the herb yielding seed, and the fruit tree yielding fruit after its kind . . ." Previously we related this plant gesture to the early Palaeozoic Era. It could equally well be said that the baby is at the Third Day of Creation.

It is difficult to relate the Fourth Day to the developing child. Perhaps, with an imaginative leap, yet within sensible bounds, it can be likened to the period immediately following the first six weeks. For, as has been described, it is at about this time that the child becomes more aware of his day-time surroundings, and, hopefully, is beginning to sleep through the night. The difference between day and night is slowly becoming more real.

"And God said, Let there be lights in the firmament of the heaven to divide the day from the night . . . And God made two great lights, the greater light to rule the day, and the lesser light to rule the night . . ."

The fish and bird gestures obviously bring us to the Fifth Day. "And God said, Let the waters bring forth abundantly the moving creature that hath life, and the fowl that may fly above the earth in the open firmament of heaven. And God created great whales and every living creature that moveth, which the waters brought forth abundantly after their kind, and every winged fowl after its kind." Anyone who looks imaginatively at these two gestures will see what is pictorially described by the writer of Genesis as the Fifth Day.

The first activity of the Sixth Day brings forth the reptiles and mammals. "God made the beast of the earth after its kind, and cattle after their kind, and everything that creepeth on the earth after its kind." Here we have imaginatively expressed, developments which began in the Carboniferous period and carried through to the Cretaceous. The baby expresses this in the reptile and quadruped gestures. He has become a "beast of the earth" and that which "creepeth on the earth."

There comes then the final act of the Sixth Day. It is the last of this phase of creative activity, for we learn in Chapter Two that on the Seventh Day, God rested.

Let us look carefully at this mighty creative gesture. "And God said, Let us make man in our image, after our likeness; and let them have dominion over the fish of the sea, and over the fowl of the air, and over the cattle, and over all the earth, and over every creeping thing that creepeth upon the earth.

"So God created man in his *own* image, in the image of God created he him; male and female created he them. And God blessed them . . ."

The child's first step mirrors this final creative act. It shows the work of the Spirit as it takes dominion over all that has gone before. The previous forms have been transcended, and through the erect posture, *man* comes into being. Now, and only now is there the possibility for creative work to be done on earth. Man is indeed made in the image of God. He is the only creature on earth able to create. [1]

In whatever way we look at the child, we are brought into contact with the great mysteries of life. People of olden days expressed these in images. It is easy to dismiss such images as the fantasies of primitive people. However, through an observation of the child, their meaning can become visible. It is during the early years that the child also expresses his experiences in images, for he then has the same pictorial consciousness as people of old. In the next chapter we will look at his drawings and ponder on their meaning.

Acknowledgement

In a series of lectures on Embryology, Dr Karl König described a correlation between the embryonic development of a human foetus and the so-called "Days of creation." In my own work, I have observed a similar correlation between the baby's body gestures and the Days of Creation starting from the Third Day. These observations form the content of this chapter. I have added the First and Second Days as taking place in utero for the sake of completion.

My observations were stimulated by reading Dr König's lectures, and I gratefully acknowledge their source.

Chapter Nine
Coming In from the Cosmos

The young child portrays with supreme artistry his experience of coming in from the cosmos and taking hold of his body. His drawings and paintings are a spontaneous expression of this process. They have a dynamic style and unabashed simplicity which ring true.

"Probably there is hardly anything so instructive regarding what is happening in early childhood as this demonstration of the actual, invisible process pouring straight out of his organism in an abundance of scribbles, drawings and coloured painting." So writes Wolfgang Schad.[1] And in describing the early 'scribble' of the two year old, Michaela Strauss says, "Big loops that came from far spaces are first created by the child; these constitute the overture in which all the main themes are already intoned. In his drawings the child reveals realms with which at this early age he is still very intimately connected."[2]

In her book *Understanding Childrens's Drawings*, Michaela Strauss illustrates her theme by drawing on the lifelong work of her father, Hanns Strauss,[3] her own wealth of experience, and her knowledge of child development as outlined by Rudolf Steiner. Out of these sources she asks, "Can the variety of forms in the dynamic of young children's writing, 'strokes-scribbles', 'loop-scribbles', and 'circle-scribbles' (H. Meyers) really be explained out of the mechanism of function only?" She explains that just as the baby's "first babbling is unconnected with particular racial or national characteristics, (so) this first picture writing is also universally human. In this early period of the first seven years, the language of symbols is the same the whole world over."[4] Surely this portrays archetypal forms, not mere mechanical functioning.

It would seem salutary then, to look at some of these drawings to gain further insight into our theme of incarnation. This is not merely because it happens to be 'interesting' but primarily because it enables a truer understanding of the child and his needs.

It was Johannes Kepler who observed " . . . that God in his firm decree chose the elements of straightness and of the curve to paint the divinity of the Creator into the world."[5] These were the primal gestures of creation. It is not surprising therefore that "'A circling spiralling force and a force that moves up and down' (H. Strauss 1932) shows us the two paths of primeval movement in the symbolic language of children's drawings. The 'whirl of circles' and the 'archetypal cross' are formed out of these two creative principles . . . The movement appears to have come from far away and comes to rest on the paper. It curves in from far spaces with the aim of concentrating rapidly towards the middle . . . Up to the third year – unless there are exceptional circumstances – we only encounter spirals that move from outside inwards."[6]

Ben: 2 years – Out in the cosmos.

Here we are in the realm of the revolving planets. It is a cosmic picture, clearly revealing the young child's experience of 'coming-in'. Strauss shows these forms to be typical of children under three years – that is, before there has developed a clear awareness of their own 'I-ness'. To begin with, there is still a oneness with the infinite, while at the same time, a seeking to come-in, to find a centre on the earth.

Joanna: 2½ years – Seeking to come in.

The other motif common to this early age is the upright cross. "The symbol of the cross documents standing in space. His orientation comes from a new impulse."[7] This is the impact of the ego, which, as shown in the two previous chapters, ever strives towards the upright. The child draws crosses as he perfects his ability to walk, and experiences himself erect in space. Later, the cross is extended to become a star; and a point is placed in the circle. This is achieved soon after three years.

Ester: 3 years – Standing erect.

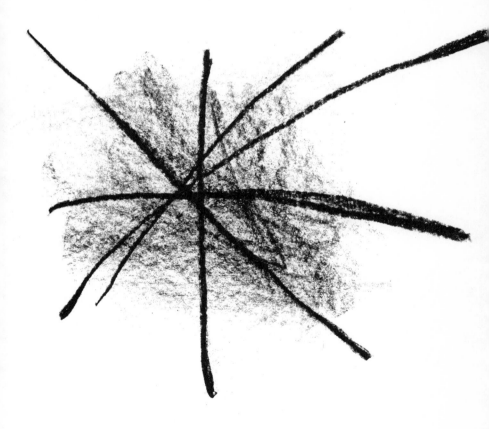

Fergus: 4½ years – The cross has become a star.

The child at this stage has a clear perception of himself as a separate entity – that is, separate from Mother and from the surrounding environment. He is able to say "I" fully conscious of what it implies. His journey towards earth consciousness has taken a mighty leap forward. He experiences *himself* in the world. The circle must now have a centre.

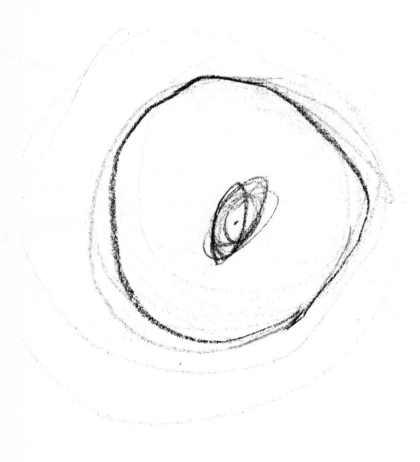

Timothy: 3½ years – I in the centre.

It is now, "after the third year (that) the circle and the crossing are fused into a unity, and they appear in the most diverse variations until the fifth year and beyond.

"The circle, with its centre fixed by means of a point or cross, describes the life situation of the child at this age. He uses these to show his relation to inner and outer space, and he puts a point or a cross in the centre of the inner space to represent himself. In both these symbols he illustrates for the first time his experience of the ego and of the world about him. The point and the cross within a circle represent the 'I-form'."[8]

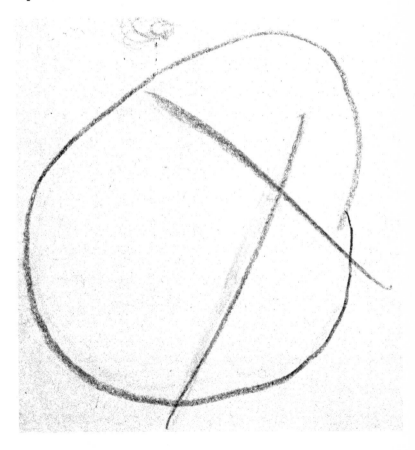

Timothy: 3½ years – The I-form, cross in circle.

Much could be said and shown to illustrate further stages on the way. There are the tree-men, first showing mainly head, for as noted earlier, the ego first builds the head organization.

Elizabeth: 4 years – Tree man.

Later there come ladders, real spinal columns and rib cages, as the child experiences the forces of growth moulding the various parts of his body. Michaela Strauss expresses it thus. "The original flowing element hardens and forms a scaffolding resembling a skeleton. In this way the 'ladder' arises. It is marked out rhythmically with subdivisions. The spinal column is divided up and the ribs encompass the chest. The rib cage has arisen in picture form."[9]

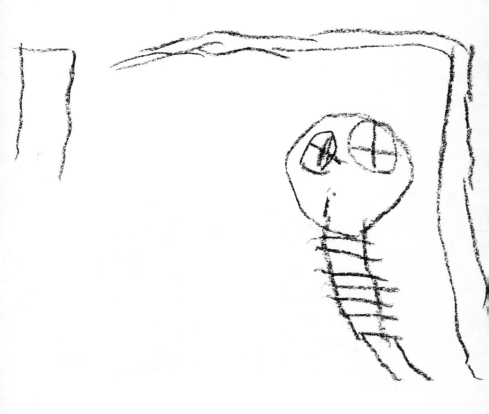

Dylan: 4¼ years – Ladder man.

We must also include the rainbow. Of all the drawings done by children it is perhaps the most telling. The rainbow spans the sky, and for the child is a reality of the heavenly sphere. He draws it and paints it, and puts himself in it. It is a bridge leading from the cosmos to earth. To begin with, the child puts himself at the top of the bow; later he shows himself on the downward slope or on earth. Here he is either at the end of the bow or underneath the arc. What could be a clearer statement of the child's inner experience of his cosmic origin and 'descent' to earth!

Jinta: 4¼ years – Down the rainbow to earth.

Alison: 6 years – Walking down the rainbow, and on earth.

It is tempting to linger amongst these many fascinating pictures, but a true grasp of their worth is best gained by a study of Michaela Strauss's book oneself. Let us be content with one more motif, that of the house.

"In no other motif can one see the multiple experiences in the process of human incarnation so clearly as in the motif of the house. On the one hand the process of moving into the house leads to becoming shut off. One is now completely dependent on oneself. On the other hand, when one has taken possession of the house, the door to the world opens from inside. By means of these drawings the child shows us a path that leads through heights and depths, joy and sorrow, good fortune and bad."[10]

Julian: 5 years – The house.

The child is now a little over four years of age. It is the great time for building wendy houses (sometimes referred to as cubby houses), for entering them confidently and happily, or creeping in in fear. "It is a game where one builds up around one the world one experiences."[11]

The house is the expression of the child's world. It can contain doors and windows that open on the world, or be completely shut in; it can be a house of friendly people or a place of fear.

Julian: 5 years – The house, smiling people.

The shape of the house changes as the child becomes more and more orientated to earth. "The child moves out of his (former) cosmically-rounded dwelling into his earthly house of the cube. The narrowing down in the perception of cosmic realms through the acquiring of self-hood – the process of becoming an 'I' – resembles an encapsulating of the soul. The house-form arising from this is based on the right angle."[12]

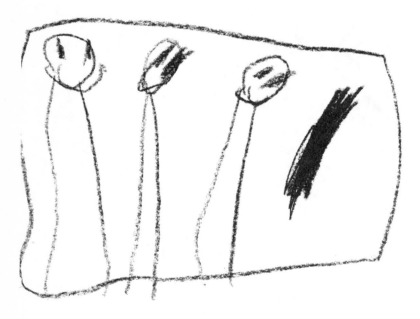

Ingrid: 4 years – The house based on the right angle.

Here, safely in his house, we will reluctantly leave the child and his drawings. We have learned of how he experiences this coming into the world, how he first of all depicts the cosmic spheres from which he knows he has come. Has this a lesson for us? It certainly has. Let us add an epilogue to this chapter and consider sex education!

Epilogue

The conflicting opinions of those concerned with sex education for young children, highlight the diversity of thought on this much-discussed subject. What is to be the approach of one who recognizes the reality of a process of incarnation, and furthermore has had this confirmed by a study of children's drawings?

The child's early portrayal of the whole revolving world of planets shows his experience of being 'out there'. His first drawings show no consciousness of the earth which physically surrounds him. Should not this experience of a heavenly origin be incorporated into sex education if it is to have any meaning for the pre-school child? If this is not done, the whole edifice of anatomical and biological detail simply has no meaning; it is contrary to the child's own inner knowing.

There is the age-old question "Where did I come from, Mummy?" – or, more likely for the modern child, "How did the baby get into your tummy, Mummy?" It is a precious moment, for it gives the opportunity to weave a wondrous story.

Before our baby was born, she lived amongst the stars. The sun and moon and rainbow were her special friends.

During the day, the sun shone his light into all the corners of heaven, and the little baby danced merrily on the sunbeams.

In the evening, the yellow moon came to greet her, and at night while she slept, the stars and the moon watched over her.

Sometimes she looked down to the world and saw other babies smiling at their Mother and Daddy; and she often longed to a have a Mother and Daddy of her own. She told her friends about it.

"We will help you find a special Mother and a special Daddy for your very own" they said. "But you must come back and visit us every night."

"Oh, I will" said the little baby gladly.

Then her friends gave her lovely presents. The sun gave his golden warmth; the stars gave their bright light; the rainbow clothed her in shining colours; and the moon wove a silver thread so she would always be able to find her way back.

While all this was going on, Mother and Daddy heard a whisper from heaven, and knew the little one was coming. They hugged and kissed each other with happiness.

Soon the baby arrived. She had travelled down a sunbeam. Then with love, which makes everything possible, Mother tucked the tiny one into her tummy, not far away from her heart.

At first she was a very very tiny baby, but in Mother's tummy she grew and grew. Soon she was big enough to come and live with us, and then Mother helped her find a special way out into the world. She was so glad to slide out and find Mother and Daddy and John and Miranda waiting to greet her.

But she hasn't forgotten her friends in heaven, and they haven't forgotten her. Every night she goes to visit them. And during the day the sun sends his warm beams down to the earth, and sometimes the rainbow comes to visit her too.

This is a pictorial representation of a truth which can be verified by those able to make spiritual scientific research. It is presented at a young child's level of understanding, and is adequate for the pre-school years. It is given here as an example only. For, imaginative parents will be able to tell their own story and perhaps, with the child's help, make it into a book and illustrate it.

When the child is older, appropriate additions or metamorphoses can be made to the story according to the child's degree of maturity. Sensitive parents will be able to decide what is necessary.

It must not be thought that the above pictorial representation is 'unrealistic' and therefore has to be 'got rid of' by the child later on. The essential meaning underlying such a story remains true for all time. Certainly, it needs to be recast from time to time as the child develops. This knowledge of a spiritual origin lays a firm and sure foundation for a child. It is the best preparation for giving additional biological information to explain the origin of the physical body.

Sex education during pre–school years should be an imaginative and joyous experience for parents and child.

> From boundless cosmic regions
> From sounding starry spaces
> Our child has sought and found us
> We welcome him to earth.

Acknowledgement

In this chapter I have liberally used the book *Understanding Children's Drawings* by Michaela Strauss. Without that, this chapter could not have been written, and I gratefully acknowledge my debt to its author.

Chapter Ten
Taking in the World - 1

There are two main ways in which we take in the world. Through food, we take the produce of earth right into our organism; and through the impressions of our senses the world flows into us.

The young child is deeply affected by both of these ways. A chapter will be devoted to each. We will start with food.

In considering nutrition it is essential to have a good knowledge of the child's nutritive needs and the chemical composition of the various foods. Only then will the body be adequately nourished. This is one aspect of the child's diet. It is well documented and there is an abundance of information readily available. Therefore, further comment on this aspect is unnecessary. This does not imply that it is considered to be relatively unimportant. On the contrary, it is obviously of the utmost importance if the child is to remain in good health and thrive.

But as well as this there are two other aspects which must also be considered if one is to have a complete picture of infant feeding. One of these is the life element of the food, (see Appendix D) and the second, the relationship of the child's diet to the growth of consciousness – or, expressed differently, the effect of food on the process of incarnation. These aspects of child nutrition are equally as important as the first. They will form the content of this chapter.

In approaching nutrition from this point of view, we must ensure that the infant's food contains maximum life-forces as well as being chemically suitable. This we will consider a little later. It will also be readily seen that the child's diet must be such that there will be a co-ordination between bodily needs and the needs of the spirit; body growth and the incarnation process must work hand-in-hand. To be able to achieve this, it is necessary to understand the *nature of the food*. If this is used as a yardstick, it will be found that the child's nutritive needs are fully met.

We will start at the beginning –

Breast Feeding

Over the past decade it has become widely recognized that breast feeding has, from every point of view, unique advantages over artificial feeding. There is now such a comprehensive literature on this subject that no need exists for details to be given here. The reader who wishes to obtain detailed information is referred to a Nursing Mothers' group. Most of these have a wealth of information available on all aspects of this 'womanly art'.

Here we will deal with two aspects not usually considered. First, we will briefly allude to the *sensory* advantages of breast feeding and then will deal with these fully in the next chapter. This is an aspect which receives all too little attention, yet is of tremendous importance; for, as we will see, breast feeding fulfills the three most important sensory needs of the baby under six months.

But there is something even more important; there is the *essential nature of breast milk*. That must be understood in its relationship to our theme.

In describing the fundamental difference between man and animal, Rudolf Steiner, in one brief sentence laden with significance said, "Animal is soul, man is spirit."[1] Are we not justified then, in assuming that human milk will have a very different *nature* from animal milk; that human milk will contain a spiritual quality, and animal milk a soul quality? In reference to milk, Rudolf Hauschka says, "milk then, welcomes the heavenly being of the child to earth and makes it an earth citizen without interfering with its belonging as well to the whole solar system."[2] Here Hauschka is referring to all milks, but his statement applies most particularly to breast milk, for this natural 'welcoming' food, more than anything else, guides the child to earth, and at the same time keeps him in touch with the wider cosmos. Down the ages mothers have strongly sensed the uniqueness of breast milk[3] and have had an intense feeling for its special qualities. It was Carl Jung who, after many years of pondering spoke of "the rationality of feeling", and went on to say ". . . it becomes quite clear that feeling values and feeling judgements – that is to say, our feelings – are not only reasonable, but are also as discriminating, logical and consistent as thinking."[4]

Therefore, without apology, let it be firmly stated that breast feeding allows the infant to remain connected with and open to the heavenly forces of his origin. To return to Wordsworth, it can be said that breast feeding preserves the consciousness of – "heaven lies about us in our infancy." It was this knowledge that was felt deeply within the hearts of women of olden times and which many mothers today are regaining.

The final point to be considered in breast feeding is the need for rhythm. By about three months of age most babies have found their own individual pattern. Demand feeding has given way to a fairly clearly recognised rhythm. If this does not occur naturally, it is desirable for Mother to help establish it. This can be encouraged by offering a bottle of diluted fruit juice now and then, instead of giving the breast continuously. This allows breast feeds to be spaced more regularly – say at three to four hourly intervals, making approximately five to seven feeds over 24 hours. The tremendous importance of rhythm in nutrition is dealt with in the Appendices. (See Appendix H.) It is an essential component of a healthy life and needs to be established right at the beginning. We will be considering it again later on.

Weaning

Over the past one or two decades there has been a marked swing to prolonged breast feeding; that is, to allowing the baby to choose his own time for weaning, and this has often meant extending the feeding period well into the second or third year. It is a pleasurable experience for Mother and a comfort to the baby. We must examine it carefully.

Traditionally, the practice of prolonged breast feeding was most marked in tribal cultures; for the people instinctively knew that this helped prepare the child for a tribal consciousness. (See Appendix I.) Here, the connection with Mother and the extended family went well beyond bonding; a real binding to the tribe took place.

Within the tribal law there is no possibility of freedom, for the law of the ancestors is inexorable. The tribe is a living complex organism, and it is this which is the unit, not the individual. There is a group consciousness and individual ownership is unknown.[5]

Since those old tribal days, man's consciousness has taken a great leap forward. Today, there is a strong consciousness of self. Every human being has the possibility to develop his own Individuality and seek for freedom. This is the experience of "I am",[6] not the Group Soul. It leads to the possibility of recognizing "you are", and eventually "we are" – in freedom.

Prolonged breast feeding belongs to a past consciousness. It cannot be described as harmful, yet one questions its wisdom for the modern child. The comfort and pleasure it gives is a soul experience for both Mother and baby. If we consider only that and the nutritive value of the milk, we have not the complete picture of the child's needs in view – only two thirds! For as we have seen, the fundamental truth of the child is the incarnation of his spirit and the development of a consciousness suitable for his *present day* needs. Unless we consider that as a primary focus and apply it to all our child care practices, we will not arrive at the truth of the matter, nor achieve a true art of parenthood for our times.

In the Gabriel Centre mothers are encouraged (but not 'pressurized'!) to wean before the baby becomes aware of what's going on, before he comes to regard his Mother's breast as his own possession. This means gradually reducing the number of breast feeds during the second half of the first year and completing the process by about the 9th to 10th month. Mothers who have done this have described the emergence of a "new relationship" with the child, and one perceptive young mother observed that the baby had become "more of an individual." We will see in Chapter Thirteen that the baby is still connected with the Mother in other ways. We will consider the 'Madonna's Cloak'.

Let it be stated once more for emphasis, this is not a matter of dependence or independence; it is a matter of *consciousness* – of preparing the child for "I am".

The Bottle Fed Baby

There are very rare occasions[7] when one meets a mother who has confidently expected to feed her baby, has prepared her soul and body for this joyful experience, yet finds she is not able to do so. Sometimes it is badly inverted nipples, sometimes a slow let-down reflex which causes the baby to become impatient, often pulling off the breast or refusing to suckle altogether. On other occasions there is simply an inadequate supply of milk, and the infant begins and continues to lose weight. The anxiety of the mother compounds the situation until the milk fails completely. More rarely still, there is the mother who has effortlessly fed several older siblings, yet is unable to feed a later baby.

What can explain these situations? Surely it is more than hormones and physiology. Here one must look carefully at the child, observing every nuance of expression, every gesture. Then sometimes one gains an insight, a revelation that enables one to ponder on the destiny of such a child; to ask oneself, "does this human spirit need to incarnate more rapidly? What are the challenges that are being sought?"

Perhaps it is in this direction that the answer lies.

Then such a child must be given a milk which is fresh and unadulterated, and contains maximum life forces; and today it is extraordinarily difficult and usually well-nigh impossible to find this. Here lies a major problem for the parents of the bottle fed baby.

Like breast milk, fresh cows' and goats' milk carry an abundance of living forces; but today many people have no confidence in these animal milks for they are regarded as being allergy producing. This is certainly true for some babies, but it by no means applies to all.

Earlier this century, fresh cows' milk was the chosen food for the bottle fed baby. It was 'modified' according to the baby's age and weight. Then, as scientists came more and more to understand the difference in chemistry between human and animal milks, it became common practice to adapt cows' milk to more nearly resemble the composition of breast milk. Thus the milk formula arose.

Valiant attempts have been made to perfect these products, yet as they come more and more under the scrutiny of modern scientific methods, one finds much that is disturbing. For example, the super-heating process (roller-drying), used to produce some infant formulae, causes the inactivation and deterioration of lysine in the milk powder.[8] (The spray drying process is much less harmful). Lysine is an essential amino acid, having a vital role to play in the assimilation of all other amino acids. Professor Fink of the University of Cologne and Bonn, showed that the death rate of rats fed with roller-dried milk was as high as 76%.[9] However, it is not only the protein that is adversely affected. It has also been found that very high temperatures, and even boiling for five minutes or longer, significantly reduces the thiamin content of milk (50% was lost); and the "Vitamin B12 was almost completely destroyed."[10] This is in contrast to the process of pasteurization which causes relatively little damage. "Losses of Vitamin B12 at low temperature or flash pasteurization ranked between 10 – 15%."[11]

These and many other findings make today's practice of feeding infants with dried milk powders (infant formulae) a highly questionable matter.

We must also ask if the adaptation process has any effect on the milk's life forces? Can this be scientifically shown? These are crucial questions, and they are questions which have not even been considered by the majority of scientists today. Yet the young infant's future health and well-being depend largely upon them. (The reader is urged to read again Appendix D, and consider the statement of two courageous researchers, Dr Eugen and Lilly Kolisko – "We have developed a specific method of research which enables us to find the various *forces* hidden in the substances . . . ".)

To really grasp the significance of the fundamental difference between the life element and the material component of food demands the courage to explore new dimensions of knowledge. (See Appendix J.) This is what is urgently needed by today's scientists concerned with infant feeding.

The Introduction of Food

At about six months of age, sometimes a week or so earlier, most babies indicate their readiness to accept food in addition to milk; and this seems an appropriate time to make a start.[12] Often a few teeth have cut through or are on the way, and it is now that parents notice the baby's increasing interest in the world around him. Obviously this is the time to help him take a further step along his earthly path; and here, as stated above, there must be a co-ordination between the processes active in his body and spirit. As we have seen this involves an understanding of the nature of food. We will start with fruit.

Fruit

Fruit blossoms are fertilized by the bees, and this give the fruit itself a special quality. For the life of the beehive is most wisely and harmoniously organized. Steiner, in his lectures on bees, describes them as living "in an atmosphere completely pervaded by love."; and relates "the whole wonderful activity within the hive to the life of love, to that part of life connected with the planet Venus."[13]

It is this 'atmosphere of love' which the bee takes to the fruit blossoms (and other flowers), caressing, as it were, the blossom, bestowing on it a glimpse of the higher life of soul. For the bee, of course, has a sentient life. It is a creature of soul. It is interesting to note that the temperature in a beehive is exactly that of human blood.

Thus are the fruits exalted above mere minerality. They embody the caress of the bee. It is no wonder that Hauschka describes them as having "moral qualities reflected in matter."

Furthermore, the stoned fruits and apples and pears, etc. seem hardly connected to the earth, so thin is the stalk which connects them to the branch. To observe an apple hanging on the tree is to gain the impression of something whose nature is above the earthy.

All fruits have originated from the rose, and carry the rose nature within them. This flower has always occupied a special place in the hearts of men and women, and is connected with the deepest Mysteries of life.

Thus fruits have a very special place in our diet. They are the ideal food to first be introduced to the baby. They are best given when in season, ripe and uncooked.

Grains

Grains (cereals) are quite different from fruits. They have a relationship with the lily, and embody this nature within them. Here there is no soul element for they are wind pollinated. One could characterize them by saying that they contain the purity of the lily.

The grains can be considered in their relationship to the elements. For example, oats have a relationship to fire (warmth); wheat to the solid earth; rye to the heaviness of water (think of rye bread!); and barley to air (light). Hauschka describes these four grains as the main European cereals, and contrasts them to rice of the east and potatoes (also a carbohydrate) of the west. The latter originated in America.[14]

Rice is 'non-earthy' in its nature, being related to the watery realm and to light. (It grows in watery paddy fields and contains silica). Steiner describes it as belonging typically to the old Eastern consciousness that said, "all matter is maya, the only reality is spirit." As the staple diet of the east, it has helped the people there, from most ancient times, to be more orientated to the reality of spirit than to the physical reality of earth.

The potato on the other hand, grows right in the earth. It is not truly a vegetable but a tuber, and moreover, it belongs to the family of nightshades as does also the tomato, capsicum and egg-plant. Steiner connects the potato with the earthiness, materialism and technology of the west. In its nature, it is the polar opposite of rice. Between these two stand the four European grains mentioned above.

What has all this to do with infant feeding?

The importance of warmth for the young child has already been mentioned. In oats we have a cereal which has a connection with this warmth element, and therefore, of the European grains, it is the least earthy in its nature. Oatmeal porridge is an ideal follow-on to the fruits.

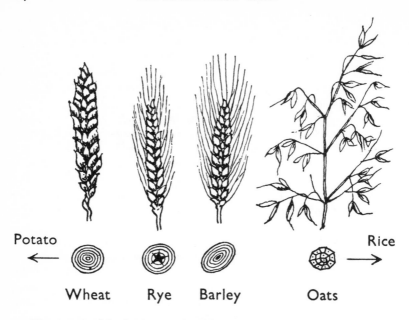

Potato   Rice

←   →

Wheat   Rye   Barley   Oats

The nature of the four types of grains and its expression in the smallest details of their form, the starch kernels. From *Nutrition* by Rudolf Hauschka, Stuart & Watkins, London 1967.

Earth	Wheat	rich in calcium salts
Water	Rye	rich in potassium salts
Air	Barley	rich in silicic acid
Fire	Oats	rich in magnesium salts

It can be made from a ground meal or finely chopped flakes, cooked with a mixture of cows' or goats' milk and water, and introduced one or two weeks after starting fruits.

Other grains can follow – millet, rice, ground wheat or baby muesli the basis of which is a collection of grains. Caution is needed with rye for its heaviness may be too demanding for a very young digestive system. It is better given towards the end of the first year rather than as an introduction.

Most people give the grains at breakfast time, and as the child grows he can share in the morning "porridge", should other members of the family be having it.

Vegetables

Now we come to the vegetables; and here we must distinguish between those that grow above the ground, and those which grow below it. In the first category we have those with a fruity nature such as pumpkin, butter-nut marrow, zucchini, squash etc; those with a leafy nature such as brussel sprouts, spinach and silver beet; and those with a flowery nature – cauliflower and broccoli. In the second category there are, for instance, carrots and parsnips.

Vegetables are truly connected with the earth. They either sit on it or are buried under it. They provide an excellent food to follow after the cereals, for they help the child to gain a real connection with the earth. Yet, unlike meat, eggs and mushrooms, they do not bring this earth influence too strongly. As a general rule, it is good to start with those above the ground and then after a few weeks, introduce roots. The former can first be given at about seven months.

An exception to this is in the case of those children whose head is large in proportion to their body size. Their fontanelle is usually large and sometimes does not fully close until after eighteen months. These children are slow incarnators (one could say, dreamy-eyed idealists!). A balance can be brought about by giving them root vegetables earlier than usual.

The polar opposite of these children are the active small-headed children with a rapidly-closing fontanelle. They develop rapidly in skills such as sitting up, crawling and walking, often have small weight gains, and are literally 'into everything'. They can be helped by generous amounts of fruit, and fruity, leafy and flowery vegetables. Roots should be given later than usual, and then only sparingly. If we understand the relationship betwen the plant and our three human body systems of head, chest, and metabolic, then, with diet, we can bring about a more harmonious balance for these children. (See Appendix K.)

Vegetables should always be cooked for young children. Fruits, as mentioned earlier are best given ripe and uncooked, although cooked apple and pear are good 'starters', for their texture is readily acceptable to most babies.

Meat - Animal, Fowl and Fish

Let us put before ourselves a picture of the bullock. Heavy, its four feet firmly on the ground, head pointing to the earth, enormous solidity, totally incapable of any lightness of foot (as for instance has the cat and horse), it presents a picture of a creature chained inexorably to the solid earth. There is a toughness about it for its flesh hardens rapidly. We are not aware of this because of the wide-spread use of 'tenderizers', but anyone who has grown up in the country knows that meat from an over mature bullock is like tough hardened leather. The sheep to a lesser extent has the same characteristics. It also is solidly anchored to the earth.

It is no wonder then, that meat brings the child rapidly and solidly into material heaviness, depriving him of his connection with the higher realms. It is the perfect preparation for a hardened materialism in later life. The child's whole body is hardened at a time when the ego is preparing it to be a fitting instrument for his soul and spirit. It is like a potter trying to work with hardened clay. Here lies a foundation for a later selfish aggressiveness and inflexibility.

It is the very greatest help to a child not to be given red meat in the early years up to the age of six or seven. The most important period is during the first three years, (the significance of the first three years will be dealt with in Chapter Thirteen) and if meat eating parents can wait until then, that is something good accomplished for the child. When it is introduced, it is best to start with lamb, for the 'little lamb' has a gentle yet frisky nature and has not yet fully taken into itself the solidity of the sheep.

For those parents who fear that the child will not have adequate protein for health and growth, a little chicken can be given sometime in the second year. The bird belongs to the air element and is not bound and anchored to the earth. Here it is important to buy a chicken that has run free and been fed on natural foods. People able to keep their own hens are fortunate in this respect.

Fish belonging to the watery element is also suitable. We are told by those who have knowledge of these things that deep sea fish is less contaminated by chemical wastes than are others.

However, neither fowl nor fish is necessary for any healthy normal infant during the first year, for the child who has an adequate intake of milk,[15] cottage or ricotta cheese and yoghourt will receive adequate protein for his needs; and this applies throughout the early years, for milk is a complete protein. Many of the 'Gabriel Babies' grow up in vegetarian families, and have beautiful body development. Meat is certainly not a nutritional necessity, and especially in the first seven years.

The above remarks apply to the pre-school child. They are not an argument in favour of vegetarianism. Meat eating in adult life is an individual matter.

Eggs

To understand the nature of eggs we must go back in history to the old Fertility Festivals. Here eggs played a prominent role, for they have a connection with fertility. At Easter time we celebrate what could be described as a fertilization of our whole planet,[16] and so we have Easter eggs.

Eggs therefore bring a strong impulse to become fertile, and both fertilized and unfertilized eggs carry this influence. Given early to a child they encourage an early puberty. On the physical level, they are high in cholesterol, and this also is a danger.

It is therefore undesirable to give eggs in any form during the first year, and preferably not as a whole egg during the first three years. But fanaticism and rigid rules must be avoided, and if Mother has prepared a dish containing egg for the family meal, then the common sense thing to do is to include the youngest member of the family provided he is over a year old.

After three years, eggs can be introduced cautiously, small amounts once or twice a week, gradually increasing over a period of some months to a whole egg. One or two eggs weekly is enough during the pre-school years. At this stage they are a valuable addition to the diet.

Milk and Honey

Let us observe the cow – or better still, a herd of cows lying in a paddock chewing the cud, their heavy bodies almost merging with the ground. Here we have a picture of creatures firmly anchored to the earth. In the section on meat we considered how different are the light-footed animals – the galloping horse, deer, and the stealthy feline. It is well known that the cow consumes an immense amount of food in relation to its body weight; and let us consider too, the value of cow manure for the earth. One gains an impression that in the cow nature and earth forces are inextricably woven together.[17] Is it any wonder then, that Rudolf Steiner describes cows' milk as the ideal food to help the child in his process of incarnation![18]

Milk, in contrast to the flesh of the animal, is more related to the pure life forces of the plant kingdom, and expresses the animal nature very weakly.[19] It therefore helps bring the child into incarnation in an appropriate way, not anchoring him too firmly in earth forces at an early age.

From this point of view, every child needs fresh milk during the first seven years of life, (that is, after weaning from the breast), and the ideal milk is that derived from the cow, a creature exuding a peaceful and harmonious soul nature.

Unfortunately, today many children are denied this essential food and instead are given a 'milk' made from the legume family – soya beans. As we will see, this brings influences of a totally different nature, the long term effect of which is yet to be seen and understood.

Fresh unadulterated milk from a herd of cows that has grazed on bio-dynamically fertilized pastures, is a gift of Nature to every child; a gift which not only nourishes his body and brings calming influences to his soul, but also helps his spirit on its journey towards earth-being.

In the bee we see a creature whose whole orientation to the earth is the polar opposite to that of the cow. The bee belongs to the elements of air and warmth; it gives the impression of actually shunning the solid earth. (Consider how different are the snail and grasshopper!). The bee's sacrificial work of fertilization, the gift of its labours to the hive, all speak a very different language from that of the earthy cow.

In honey, we have a food, the very nature of which helps us gain an orientation to non-earthly realms.

Furthermore, honey is a living food, and is described by Dr Eugen and Lilly Kolisko as "a very valuable substance which is scarcely enough appreciated as far as its nutritive and remedial qualities are concerned."[20] They described it as having a variety of formative forces hidden within it.

Here we see the ideal food for older people, when restorative forces of the ego are waning; and more than any other food, honey helps us to be orientated towards higher realms of existence.

Rudolf Steiner advised that honey should not be given to very young children, or if so, sparingly, for its nature is in distinct contrast to that of milk, the true food of the child. However, after the age of seven years, honey can be used a little more liberally, giving the child the benefit of its life forces and nutritive qualities.

We could sum up this section by saying that cows' milk helps the child in finding an orientation to earth; and honey helps and sustains the older person in finding a connection with heaven. Both are essential foods according to age.

Nightshades, Mushrooms and Legumes

Potatoes, tomatoes, capsicum and eggplant, as already mentioned, belong to a family of poisonous plants, the nightshades; and while the above foods are not poisonous themselves, there is this tendency there. The normal protein forming process in the seed, takes the abnormal course of making alkaloids, and the nightshades have an above-average nitrogen content. As adults with an ego fully incarnated, we are able to deal with this influence; but for a child whose ego is in the process of incarnation and body building, it is a different matter.

Nightshades, particularly potatoes, should not be given in the baby's first year, and should be used with caution throughout the preschool period.

Mushrooms are not a vegetable but a fungus. One feels their earthiness and erratic habits of growth to be somehow too overpowering for the young child; and like some of the nightshades, the toadstool is poisonous. They are a strange family, and one asks, "can the child cope with such an influence so early in life?"

Legumes will be mentioned very briefly, for it is difficult to describe their nature without going into far-reaching details.

Suffice to say that Rudolf Steiner characterizes them as having distinct animal qualities, observable in the kidney shape of bean seeds and their high protein content – they are able to assimilate nitrogen directly from the air. Hauschka, after going into details, sums them up by saying "The protein they contain is more truly animal than animal milk."[21]

For adults their high protein is a valuable nutrient,[22] but how will this 'animalistic' influence affect the tissues of the baby's body?

Soya beans from which soya milk is derived belong to this family. One of their significant characteristics is the fact that in the active bacteria nodules in the root, they make a red dye which resembles the red dye of the blood. It is called Leghaemoglobin. Here is manifested a truly animal tendency.[23] We will leave its effect on the young baby as a question mark.

The Toddler and Onwards

As the child grows older, diet is a matter of good-quality food and common sense. *It should never be a matter of fanaticism.* The baby becomes a toddler and can share the family meal within reason. A greater variety of foods can be introduced – dried fruits, wheat germ, herbs such as mints, marjoram, thyme and rosemary which have a warming effect on the digestive tract, a variety of breads such as rye which is a good form of protein, later, nuts, and later still as we have seen, eggs and peas and beans.

If parents keep in mind the above principles, and prepare the child's meal with joy and enthusiasm, having a gratitude for the food, then it will be sure to nourish him.

> "The provision of a proper diet calls
> for more than calories and vitamins;
> we need to enjoy our food if it is
> to do us good."
> John Bowlby [24]

Some Practical Matters

It is well known and hardly needs mention that stainless steel or enamel make the best saucepans. Vegetables should be prepared just before cooking, and either steamed or boiled in a little water, and for the baby, need to be cooked until soft. (They should never be fried). They can then be mashed finely or cut into chunky pieces according to the age of the child. They do not need to be sieved if given at the recommended age.

Neither should they be puréed in a blender for this ruins the texture. At this age salt should not be added, for the infant kidney is not efficient in handling high salt loads, and it is well known that salt brings about hardening processes in the body.[25] (Most hard cheeses have a significant salt content, and are therefore not suitable for young children).

When introducing food, start with small amounts, say one or two teaspoons, and increase according to the baby's appetite. After two or three weeks he will probably be taking about a quarter to half a cupful. Cereals, as mentioned earlier, are usually given for the morning feed, fruits either for midday or evening, and vegetables, starting at about seven months, make a third meal. Whether the food is given before or after breast feeding, or in between feeds is not important. The appropriate time is that most suitable for baby and Mother's daily rhythm.

Fixed rigid feeding schedules are far too regimented both for parents and child; yet, the higgeldy-piggeldyness of no pattern is equally undesirable. Between these two extremes lies the pattern of a rhythmic day, where meals take their place within the sequence of daily activities.

A rhythmic pattern of feeding for the child is highly desirable. To establish good eating habits in the early years will be a blessing to carry over into adulthood. This is a parental responsibility.

"Feeding even the healthiest people
is a responsible job, impossible
without true insight into human
nature."

Grethe Hauschka

Chapter Eleven
Taking in the World - 2

Through the windows and doorways of our senses the world flows into us and deeply affects our souls. We delight in the perfume and colour of the rose, are soothed by the harmony of music, and form concepts about what we perceive as we seek to understand the world.

But more than this, very strong sense impressions can actually affect our body. We feel 'sick in the stomach' if we are unexpectedly confronted by a repelling sight; we become pale, or may even faint with fear as the circulation of our blood is affected by hearing a terrifying sound. The fact that the body is not similarly affected by *all* sense impressions is because we are usually able to transform the impression into a soul experience; we form a concept about what we perceive, come to an understanding and make a judgement or decision. In our ability to think and form concepts we have a protective mechanism which, as it were, deflects the impressions from affecting our bodily organs, and takes it up into the soul. It is only the very strongest sense impressions that overcome this protective mechanism and actually cause physiological changes in our organs.

So it is with adults. But what of the young child? Has he also the thinking capacity to assimilate the content of what he perceives? Can he deflect the confusing kaleidoscope of impressions as they storm into him from the busy and noisy world, or do they penetrate right into his body?

Willi Aeppli in his book *The Care and Development of the Human Senses* has much to say about these questions.[1] He is speaking of early childhood; "The power of thinking and of judgement which is not yet in existence cannot form a protective dam against the storming in of sense impressions. Consequently the child is exposed with his whole body to these impressions in quite a different way, in a far more direct way than at a later age. All sense-perceptions go deeply into the organism and leave their impressions there . . . "

The young child, through his sensory organization, most truly absorbs the world right into his organism, and, as Aeppli further points out, the influences gained through the senses extend well beyond the actual organ itself. For instance, "The small child hears music less with the ear than with his whole body, which vibrates and lives in this musical element. His whole physical being is then either in harmony or disharmony."[2]

We see from the above how important it is that a young child should be surrounded by good-quality sense impressions if his organism is to be built up in a healthy way. All parents would want their child to have bodily organs which remain in good health throughout life. Good-quality sense impressions in the early years is one way to contribute to this goal. It is therefore important that we consider what *are* good quality sense impressions and what are harmful. But before doing that, let us look specifically at the sense organs themselves. We will start with the hand, an organ of touch.

Let us consider the hands of a good pianist, a juggler and an outdoor labourer. The first would have a tremendous sensitivity, the second a dexterity and the third a strength and probably a calloused roughened skin. It will be obvious that according to how the hand is used, so will it develop. There will be a fine sensitivity, a calloused roughness or a dexterity depending upon what comes to it in usage. This not only applies to the hand, but also to all sense organs. For example, eyes and ears are 'tuned' and made into sensitive instruments or are 'coarsened' according to how they are used throughout the early years.

We can now say that *according to the quality of the sense impressions received throughout the first seven years, so will the sense organs develop*. It is well known that by age seven, the child has a completely new body. Every cell has been changed. The ego has penetrated into every cell of the hereditary body, working with it, moulding it to better suit its own purpose. What can be achieved by this ego activity depends partly upon the good or harmful properties of the impressions that flow in through the child's sense organs.

Later, in Chapter Fifteen, we will deal with the close connection between our soul life and the senses; but now let us look in detail at some of the senses themselves, and attempt to differentiate between good and harmful impressions.

Rudolf Steiner, in his many lectures on this subject, speaks of twelve senses. Added to the usual five, there is a human sense for rhythm, warmth, balance, movement and so on, and we will look at several of these as well as some of the other five. Let us first consider rhythm, warmth and touch, for these three are the most important senses for the child under six months of age.

Rhythm

As we have seen previously, all life processes are rhythmic. There are great cosmic rhythms of the planets revolving around the sun, and of the sun itself in its rhythmic relationship to the stars of the zodiac. There are worldly rhythms of the seasons, of birds nesting and mating, of day and night; and there are human rhythms of heartbeat and respiration, and, as we shall see later, of the soul's unfolding.

Within these rhythms we have our being, and a state of well-being is largely dependent upon our incorporating these rhythms into our daily life. The child, as a living organism, most particularly needs to live rhythmically, and, right from the start needs the opportunity to incorporate the rhythms of life into himself. Let us emphasize by re-stating what was said in Chapter Ten – rhythm holds the balance between rigidity and the higgeldy-piggeldyness of no pattern.

For the infant, the time honoured rocking chair, cradle and lullabies help fulfil this need; also breast feeding, for while suckling, the child strongly experiences the mother's rhythmic heart beat. Later on, nursery rhymes and rhythmic songs and games give much. Above all, the child needs a rhythmic pattern to his day. Playing, sleeping and eating should take place, not as a fixed schedule, but in an ordered pattern as far as it is possible within the family's way of life. Every effort should be made to achieve this for the child, for his future state of well-being depends largely upon it.

A rhythm for going to bed is also essential, many pre-school children are not in bed until 10pm or later; they are then tired the next day, so that the pattern of their daily activities is often upset. Like all young creatures, children need adequate sleep if they are to function at optimum level. Bedtime by about 7pm is a good habit – or maybe 8 o'clock during daylight saving. The evening meal, perhaps a story, or a time with Dad, then to bed, should become a well-established rhythm in the early years.

The importance of rhythm in nutrition has already been mentioned, and this should apply from the earliest months onwards. It has been pointed out that the demand feeding of the first two or three months will usually give way quite naturally as the baby finds his own rhythm. This needs to be recognized and fostered. It should be followed by a rhythm for mealtimes.

The establishment of rhythmic patterns in the child's life is of the utmost benefit, and can be carried over as a mainstay of harmonious living in later life.

Warmth

The importance of warmth has also been briefly mentioned. Here we will explore the matter a little further.

When we observe the plant and animal kingdoms we see that growth and the care of the young are associated with warmth. The seed falls to the ground in autumn, remains dormant in the soil during the cold of winter, and only after the winter solstice when the earth begins to warm, does it sprout. The warmth of the spring sun draws it forth, and it comes up as a plant.

Amongst the birds we observe the mother hen warming the chickens under her wings and covering them with her body in the nest. The animals also provide warmth for their young. The mother cat curls her body around the kittens, the kangaroo tucks the joey into her pouch, and the foal and calf keep close to the mother's body as they run along beside her, and are warmed by her body heat. Thus does the wisdom of nature express itself.

For the human baby, warmth is also essential. If the ego is to be able to perfect the organs so that they endure in good health throughout life, there must be a well-maintained deep body warmth. For, as has already been mentioned, it is the warmth organization wherein the ego works. We have previously considered the importance of wrapping in the early months and the necessity for pure woollen singlets, pants, tights, blankets and a bonnet or hat. For a child under a year old to wear a flimsy top only (that is, no singlet, or worse still, a nappie only) is contrary to the laws of Nature however hot the weather may be. It is asking for body organ degeneration in later life. Whether the day be warm or cool, the hen tucks the chickens under her wing and the cat warms the kittens. So it should be for the human baby. Breast feeding, that truly wonderful art, helps fulfil this need also, for the infant, held close to the mother's body, experiences her warmth.

It is sometimes said that the child should be dressed according to how the mother herself feels most comfortable. This theory shows a complete lack of understanding of the difference between adult and young child. In the former, the ego is fully incarnated and is able to control the body temperature, whereas in the latter, as we have seen, the ego is in a process of incarnation and is not yet fully in charge. Here one sees the wisdom of the old adage which says that old people experience a second childhood. This is well illustrated by the inability of old people to maintain their body heat, for in their case the ego is gradually loosening its hold on the body. Grandma, with a rug over her knees gives an accurate picture of the young child's need for warmth.

Touch

From the moment of birth, and indeed before birth, the baby experiences touch. No wonder Ashley Montagu describes the skin as "the primary organ of the human infant."[3] There is the skin-to-skin bonding with mother immediately after birth, the cuddling, kissing, caressing, and again, breast feeding that all nourish this need for early tactile experiences. While breast feeding, the child feels the mother's skin, often stroking her breast while suckling. It is a wonderful communication through the sense of touch. We have already mentioned the need for soft clothes made from natural fibres, and have dealt with massage. To all this skin contact, the infant's tactile sense responds.

The older child's need for tactile experiences can be met by a friendly arm around his shoulder, and approving pat on the head, taking him on to Mother's or Dad's knee for the evening story. Being warmly kissed goodnight, and given a big hug for special occasions speaks both to senses and soul!

Throughout life these three senses remain important. During early childhood their care must be emphasized. In infancy, it is breast feeding as much as anything else that nurtures them. For the bottle-fed baby, parents need to compensate in other ways.

Eyes and Ears

After about six months of age, other senses start to become more dominant. The child begins to take in the world more strongly through eyes and ears. He has, of course, been able to see and hear all the time, but now he becomes more conscious of the world of sights and sounds.

On one of her visits to the Gabriel Centre, Helena recounted the following: "I was in the garden with Rebecca (her seven month old daughter). She was in her push chair playing with a toy. Suddenly a blackbird began to sing. Rebecca stopped her playing and obviously listened. When the bird stopped singing she turned to me and smiled as much as to say 'Wasn't that lovely, Mummy!'"

Rebecca at seven months had been conscious of the bird-song. A child of two or three months would have heard the sound, but not consciously listened to it. Rebecca had begun to take in the world through her eyes and ears.

This brings us to consider the immense importance of visual and auditory sense impressions. For eyes and ears must be 'tuned' to present the world intensely in all its great variety. As an adult the child will need eyes that truly *see* and ears that truly *hear* if he is to experience the world. It is obvious that perception of an object is a necessary pre-requisite to an experience of what it has to offer. Some people today hardly notice the world around them, whether it be a vase of flowers on a table, the wind in the trees or the night sky. They have eyes that don't truly see and ears that don't truly hear, and their inner life is correspondingly barren because of it.

To help develop sensory capacities which will enrich the child's immediate present and his adult life, means *starting at birth* with good quality sense impressions.

Much that is relevant here has already been covered in our discussion of the expectant mother's preparation and the child's special needs during the first six weeks. We have seen the importance of colour, and have noted the necessity for careful choice of pram lining and clothes, etc. As the child grows older the gentle pinks, blues and creams of infancy can give way to clear reds, yellows and stronger blues – that is, the primary colours. In Rudolf Steiner schools the walls of each classroom are painted a different colour according to the age of the children. Each year, the whole class moves to another room to be surrounded by a colour appropriate to that stage of the children's development. It is not until the mid-school years that the child is sufficiently 'earthed' to take in browns and greens as a real soul experience.

As a general guideline, it can be said that good-quality visual and auditory sense impressions are always harmonious and artistic. Nature, with her abundance of flowers, the rhythm of waves, the songs of birds, the majesty of the forest, mountain and waterfall, is the Archetypal Artist whose creations never cease to amaze us. For the young child to be introduced to such artistry and to take it deeply into himself has an upbuilding effect on his whole body. Parents can share his enthusiasm as he gazes in wonder at a beetle or looks at the stars or moon. While at the beach they can listen with him to the waves, rejoice with him in the finding of a shell. Even the simplest things, a worm in the garden soil, can be a source of fascination for a small child. Through his eyes and ears he will absorb these processes of Nature, thus enlivening in a harmonious way his sensory organization.

Good quality human sights and sounds also nourish the senses. There is Mother and Dad's smiling face and kindly encouraging word. We have mentioned lullabies and songs in relation to rhythm; and it has also been pointed out that a living voice or music is of much greater value for a child than the most sublime music on radio or tape. The former carries a living nourishing human quality, while the latter is a mechanised version of what was once alive. It has lost its power of upbuilding forces.

Indoors, an attractive picture on the wall, carefully chosen curtains and simple furnishings (that is, not a cluttered environment) all help the eyes to become sensitive to their surroundings.

It can now be asked what is to be avoided if children are to grow into adults able to truly perceive and experience the world. What is it which destroys the capacity of eyes to see and ears to hear?

Again, much has already been mentioned; the raucous shrill loud house sounds, the screeching of car brakes, traffic noise and confusion, the ugliness of shouting at another, ugly garish colours – all these constantly bombarding the child's senses bring disorder into the sensory organization and do immense harm. The senses coarsen and harden just as surely as the hand is coarsened and hardened if used in an insensitive way. This is not perceptible in the outer anatomical form of the organ, but more subtly, in its 'finest structure.'[4] It is here that the organ will be affected, and there will be a subsequent lack of sensitivity.

However, harmful as the above influences are, they pale into insignificance when one turns to consider the devastating and almost irreparable damage caused to the young child by watching television.

To grasp this fully, one must clearly understand the very great difference between the effects of adult sensory experiences and those of the child (set out at the beginning of this Chapter).

Many studies have been carried out to assess the effects of television on children[5] and this has been considered from many points of view. For instance, it is well documented that the artificial light emanating from the television screen is detrimental to health. The scientist John Ott showed the distortion caused to bean plants that were grown in front of a television set, and his work with mice is equally convincing.[6]

Dr Stuart Black Kelly of the Community Health Department of the Royal United Hospital at Bath, U.K. considers that "children's eyes need to be protected from possible television damage."[7] And again, Martin Large writes, "Constant eye movement is required for a healthy eye . . . Watching the screen is one of the most visually passive activities . . . the eyes are practically motionless."[8]

There is also the destruction of the child's capacity to concentrate. This aspect was considered by F. and M. Emery, psychologists working at the Australian National University, Canberra. Their publication *A Choice of Futures; to Enlighten or Inform*[9] states that television both "destroys the capacity of the viewer to attend . . . (and) by taking over a complex of direct and indirect neural pathways, decreases vigilance." They point out that this form of 'distraction' is just the opposite to a concentrated frame of mind. They also deal with the adverse effects of television on the nervous system and its undermining of the child's ability to develop social skills and to communicate. The phenomenon of the so-called 'computer kid', children unable to communicate with parents or peers, is a sad commentary on the above. The Emerys also make telling observations on the relationship between hyperactivity in children and television.[10]

Other authorities speak of a number of further dangers. For example, Faith Hall, speech therapist, draws attention to speech deprivation;[11] Plowdon, National Foundation for Educational Research, U.K. points to reading difficulties;[12] and Dr Edelson, Director of the Child Guidance Clinic, Bradford, U.K. reports on psychiatric disturbances.[13] Added to these, the inhibiting of the child's fantasy must be mentioned. A lack of fantasy play is sadly observable in many kindergarten children who are unable to enter into make-believe situations or play at 'dressing–up' etc.[14] As we shall see later, childhood fantasy forms one of the first foundation stones for the development of an important soul faculty.

To complete this survey, we will mention the work of Dr Mulholland, psycho-physiologist, and Dr Peter Crown, Professor of Psychology at Hampshire College, Massachusetts, U.S.A. who worked with changes in brain waves (i.e. alpha waves) in both adults and children who were engaged in viewing television. Their research brought them to the conclusion that such watching induces passivity (high frequency alpha waves). This was in contrast to similar tests carried out on children who were reading. These showed the reverse alpha pattern, indicating 'attentiveness'.[15]

All of these studies (and many more could be given) add up to a far reaching indictment of television for the young child. An important point on which such authorities agree is that it is not so much the *content* of the programme which is damaging, but the actual viewing itself. Whether the programme be 'good' or 'bad' is of minor significance.

Let it be remembered that we are speaking here of the child under seven years of age who, as we have seen, is engaged in building up his bodily organism as he incarnates gradually into every part of it.

After seven years of age, *limited* and *carefully chosen* viewing can be gradually introduced should parents wish it; for then there is a greater thinking capacity, and the bodily organs have been fully 'worked over' and developed by the ego. However, even at this age, prolonged viewing is still highly damaging, and leads to lack of concentration at school, as teachers well know. One perceptive Kindergarten director claimed to be able to tell the difference between children who watched television and those who did not. She based this on the child's capacity for creative play.

Should the above be considered biased, unjustifiable or unable to be scientifically proved (in spite of the many studies carried out by a variety of professional authorities), it may be salutary to reflect upon the many degenerative diseases today, and have the insight and courage to ask why it is that the body's organs in so many cases are unable to maintain their health and vitality? What is it that causes a deterioration in the immune system? Could it be that the body's organs have not been built up strongly enough and in a healthy way throughout childhood? Has the body been permeated through and through by destructive forces flowing in through the senses, so that every organ has been adversely affected? Many of these diseases manifest most commonly in later life; but could it be that the predisposition for their appearance is laid down in the very earliest years?

These are justifiable and pertinent questions as we look at the proliferation of degenerative diseases today. They are questions which need an answer and positive action on the part of all concerned.

Finally on this matter, let it be said that the above is not to be regarded as an anti-television tirade! It is not the medium itself that is under consideration, but *the age of the viewing child, and the amount of time spent viewing.* For old people, unable to participate fully in the affairs of life, television can be a wonderful boon, opening up new fields of knowledge and bringing the affairs of the world to an otherwise circumscribed life. Television viewing demands conscious, responsible and informed decisions.

But now let us leave this subject, and turn to another of the senses. We have several more to consider.

Movement

We have seen in Chapter Seven how the infant's feeling of body freedom (as he begins to move his limbs, crawls, toddles, runs and jumps) is a key factor in the later gaining of a consciousness of freedom. We must now consider other aspects.

Joseph Chilton Pearce, in a discussion of the human brain, points to two areas, an old and a new, (the so-called reptilian and mammalian brain on the one hand, and the neocortex on the other). He says "Were we to operate entirely out of the old-brain system (as indeed we do at first), we would be as purely instinctive as the lower species. We would have neither an open intelligence nor a flexible logic; we would have no creativity or individual personality."[16] It is the new-brain which gives us these capacities. He then explains that "The transfer from old-brain potential to new-brain actuality takes place through the infant-child's muscular body movements."[17]

We see how crucial it is then, for the child to have freedom and space to crawl, later to toddle, and later still to engage in active play activities. This does much more than develop his muscle co-ordination; it actually helps develop the brain itself.

The sense of movement brings us to consider baby exercises, the arbitrary movement of limbs in which the child's will is passive.

Those who advocate these exercises are concerned with "the awakening and development of alertness through movement."[18]

It is recommended that they should start in the earliest weeks, and at this stage, should be accompanied by "a shining mobile above his cot, a loud sounding musical rattle, and brightly coloured balls strung across his cot."[19]

Later, at three months, there should be (amongst other things) 'noisy toys,' and 'squeaky rubber toys'; and parents are advised to 'make a noise' near his cot. Now it is recommended that the child should be dressed "in as few clothes as possible; if it is warm enough, just a nappie and very soft roomy bodice, allowing him to move as much as he wants." He should be put "flat on his tummy on the ground on a foam carpet, as often as possible."[20]

All of this is aimed at stimulating the child and awakening his alertness. Further, the exercises aim to 'stretch the muscles' and give 'body awareness.' It is stated that "In the light of modern knowledge . . . the child's control of movement can no longer be left to chance, instinct or the inspiration of the moment."[21]

Much could be said to refute these practices but what has been discussed in previous chapters will clearly illustrate their tremendous harm. As in many other child-care practices today, their proponents assume that to stimulate the child in the early weeks, to awaken his alertness, is the best possible thing.

These theories and their practical application arise from a point of view devoid of any understanding of the child as a being of body, soul and spirit. There is no knowledge that the spirit needs a six weeks period of adjustment after birth, nor that body development must recapitulate all the evolutionary stages including the plant stage of the early weeks; neither is it known that the ego, *out of its own forces*, is gradually taking charge of the body, and that the child, far from having a 'body awareness' lives very much in an awareness of the cosmic spheres which he shows in his drawings. Body awareness has no place in his early experiences. As we saw right at the beginning, knowledge of the child's threefold being is fundamental if we are to prepare his soul and spirit in the true way.

In commenting on the harmfulness of baby exercises, Norbert Glas has this to say; "They may also result in an inner lack of freedom. A man who feels himself as if chained to the earth and to the world of matter, may owe this to the experience of the 'sense of movement' in his childhood when he was driven too early into the life of his limbs . . ."[22]

We will proceed without further comment!

Balance

The sense of balance enables us to maintain our body position. And this faculty, like the sense of movement, also has its inner counterpart. The practice and achievement of body balance in the toddler has the possibility of expressing itself as a 'balanced soul' in later life, a capacity to maintain one's position throughout life's challenges. Again, the child needs opportunity to practise this; and in this context, it must again be emphasized that the above exercises and also baby walkers deny the toddler the opportunity of achieving this

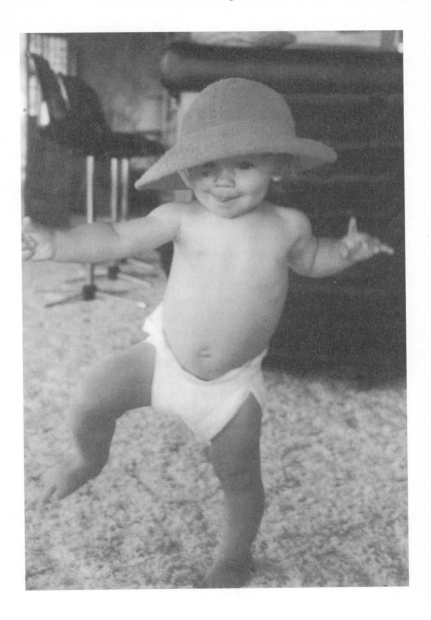

Gabrielle practising balance at 14 months.

sense out of himself. A subsequent tendency towards lack of balance in the soul, may well result.

Let us remind ourselves of the well-known fact that body and soul interact and affect each other. This is becoming more well recognized as doctors find that stress and other soul disturbances can be the cause of a number of diseases. Body and soul are a unity; and early experiences of freedom and balance in the body, can most surely manifest later as feelings of freedom and balance in the soul.

The Sense of the Other's Ego

Lastly we come to a sense which enables us to make a real contact with other people, to form friendships, to communicate and so on. Steiner calls it "the sense of the other's ego." We use it to sense the happiness or sadness of our friends, to enter into meaningful conversations with another and to share experiences with a loved one.

Lack of this sense is one of the things that brings a feeling of isolation, an inability to communicate or form friendships, and creates difficulties with relationships both at home and at work. This is a special malaise of our times, and we must therefore ask what can be done in the early years to foster this sense.

Above all, the child need *human* contacts, not the products of technology, if this sense is to develop. In infancy, it is breast feeding which lays the first foundation stone. Later come play-mates, family celebrations such as Grandma's birthday party, and the ebb and flow of family life – visits to friends, going for holidays as a family, singing Christmas carols together, and having family meals together. Meal times can be a family social event with an interchange of lively conversation. Saying grace before the meal, offering thanks for the food and asking a blessing can be enriching experience for the whole family. It is these shared human experiences which prepare the child to develop a real sense for the needs of others and to be able to joyfully relate himself to his fellow beings.

In today's rush and bustle, the practice of these things makes a demand upon parents' will, but to consciously practise them is of enormous value, strengthening to children and parents alike. For today, the sense that helps us experience and understand the other individual is brought far too little into use; in fact it is paralysed or even "systematically destroyed by modern civilization" unless we made a conscious effort to cultivate it.[23]

Finally, as we look at the world of the twentieth century and the demands that life makes upon us, it is little wonder that our senses are assaulted and brought into disharmony. Is there anything that can be done to bring a compensating healing influence into our battered sensory organization? Yes, there is; there is *art*. More than anything else, art heals our senses and keeps them healthy. It is therefore imperative that young children live within an artistic environment, and later on actually participate in an artistic activity such as painting, clay modelling, eurythmy,[24] singing,[25] or playing a musical instrument. Eurythmy is particularly beneficial for children, and more than any other art brings healing to disturbed bodies and distressed souls.

The artistic element is the therapeutic element. We all desperately need it, and children especially so.

Chapter Twelve
The Human Soul and its Functions

Deep and mysterious is the human soul, and wide ranging is its orbit. It raises us to lofty heights or drags us down into wild and surging passions. Its complexities and polarities of light and dark, love and passion, run the whole gamut of life's experiencing.

Through its feminine nature there is the tenderness of the Madonna expressed in an encompassing love for the child. Through its will force there are noble deeds or raging tempestuous destruction; and through its thinking it reaches both for the sublime and the diabolical. It is to this enigmatic member of our being that we must now turn.

Like the body, the soul needs nourishment throughout the length of life; and during the childhood years foundations must be laid so there will be capacities for purposeful action, clarity of thinking and a heart involvement in all of life's endeavours. This demands an understanding of the soul, and the nature and unfolding of its functions. Let us now turn to these matters.

If we reflect upon our inner life, we will come to see that it expresses itself in three different ways. There is our mental life, both our rational mind and imaginative pictorial thinking; there is our life of feeling ranging from sensations associated with bodily processes to the most intense feelings of love and hate; and there are will impulses involving instinctive animal-like urges on the one hand, and deeds carried out in the light of full consciousness on the other. The more we investigate our inner life and human consciousness in all its manifold expression, the more do we come to see that our soul has three archetypal ways of manifesting; it has three powers or functions to which can be related all its activities and varied forms of consciousness. These are *will*, *feeling* and *thinking*.

To be able to use these in the world, there must be a bodily basis. The soul needs an instrument through which to express itself, otherwise it is of little use to the human spirit whose servant it is. It is obvious that the brain is the bodily instrument of the thinking soul; and also obvious that the heart and whole rhythmic system serves the feeling. The idiomatic phrase "My heart feels for you," is no idle statement – it reflects a truth. The will forces of the soul use limbs and metabolic system. I 'do' with my hands; and again, the idiom of the language casts its light in the phrase, "That man has guts – he can get things done!"

Will, feeling and thinking, using limb-metabolic, rhythmic, and brain-nervous systems; thus is the connection between body and soul functions.

In the developed human being these three soul functions work together. Actions are directed by thought, and the heart is in the deed to warm and enthuse it. So it should be if we are to be truly human. But sadly, this is not always so. We often see a strong will totally or partially uncontrolled; there is the clever, highly-developed intellect often working devoid of any feeling; or there is an emotional life lacking in purpose and direction, unstable, and not able to express itself in meaningful activity. The person whose soul life suffers such imbalance is at a disadvantage in all areas of life – work, play and home. It is during the first twenty-one years that these soul functions must be prepared in such a way that there will be strength and balance in the soul, an inter-relationship of activity, thought and feeling. How are parents to ensure that this will be so for their child?

An observation of the child's physical growth reveals that the three body systems mentioned above develop in a rhythmic pattern of three periods of seven years. At first, the forces of growth work strongly on the brain and nervous system. During the first year the head grows as much as throughout the rest of life, and at seven years of age it is almost fully grown. (See Appendix L.) But during this period, the limbs are virtually useless at first, and it is not until the end of the first year or later that the legs can be used for walking. The young child only gradually gains confidence to walk and run, and it is much later that there develops a real sure-footedness.

The rhythmic system also remains comparatively undeveloped in the early years. Pulse and respiration are often irregular, and the temperature rises and falls in an unpredictable way. It is not until the primary school years that these are brought under control as growth forces work into heart and lungs. Traditionally, this was the time for rhythmic games expressed in song and dance.

"Farmer in the Dell" "London Bridge is Falling Down" and "Oranges and Lemons" were favourites down the years until superseded by the a-rhythmical inanities of Humphrey Bear and the like.

It is during the teenage years that there is a noticeable growth in the limb system. This is the great time for athletics and sports. Now too, the metabolic system matures. The time of unpredictable tummy-aches is over.

When one perceives this process of growth from the head downwards, it would be easy to assume that the unfolding of the soul faculties takes a similar direction; that is, that the child would first use his brain system of thinking, and lastly his limb system of will. This however, is obviously not so, for the infant and toddler are incapable of conceptual thought because of immaturity of brain structure, and the unfinished myelination of the brain cells.[1] This apparent paradox of body growth and soul function is resolved when, on closer investigation, a second stream of development reveals itself, one which proceeds in the opposite direction – from below upwards. This is a process of development described by A. C. Harwood as being "awake and alive in the use of an organ, no matter how imperfectly formed."[2] He coins the term "awakeness in use" for this, and says "it must be placed in its natural contrast with the stream of physical completion."[3]

As we watch the infant discovering his hands and kicking with zest, the toddler, full of activity, splashing in the bath, exploring and 'doing' and the pre-school child delighting in building, digging and climbing, we see an expression of this 'awakeness in use' of the limbs.

Likewise in the teenager there is an awakeness in the brain system as the student grapples with tertiary education and its demands on rational thinking. Joining these two is the system of heart and lungs, and here in the primary school years the stream of physical growth and that of awakeness meet.

Here a clue is emerging which will indicate the unfolding rhythm of the child's soul functions. In the activity of limbs it is the soul force of will which is manifesting; in the use of the rhythmic system, feeling is burgeoning; and in the awakeness of the head, the thinking intellect takes wing. Now we gain an insight into how we should work with the child's unfolding soul functions.

It is this bottom to top process of 'awakeness in use' which allows the physical development of the brain to proceed undisturbed. For to use something before it is fully developed hinders its completion. It is like moving into a house and cluttering it with furniture and cases while carpenters are still working upon it – that is, before it is structurally complete.

Unfortunately, this premature 'use' is the state of affairs for many children today as early education programmes teach reading and mathematics in the very earliest years. Here the child's head is cluttered with information which engages his intellect, whereas the need of his soul is for active doing-experiences which nurture his will. The harmful effects of this will only show much later – in the teenager as an 'opting-out' or in adulthood when the man is likely to lack initiative and imagination. For as a child, his soul forces will have been diverted from hands to head, and his thinking changed from imaginative pictures to rational concepts. This is a tragedy of our times.[4]

But to return to our theme . . . It can now be said that the child's soul unfolds in rhythms of approximately seven years which manifest in the order of will, feeling and thinking.

Therefore, throughout the pre-school years, the child needs opportunity to be active in his limbs, and parents are faced with the task of guiding strong will forces. These forces are then carried over into the school years and further developed. The child's activities now become suffused with feeling as the rhythmic system begins to develop; and finally, sometime after puberty, actions are able to gain clearer direction and feelings to become more controlled as rational thinking takes charge. Thus it should be for the child, and thus it can be if parents and educators are aware of these soul processes. Fortunate is the man who has all these childhood foundation stones to carry into adulthood. For him, there will most surely be an opportunity for further soul development as life's experiences unfold.

Before proceeding to consider what the above means in the practical care of the young child, let us reiterate and strongly emphasize two fundamental facts which emerge as we gaze at the child and observe the outward expressions of his soul.

At the outset, let us be quite clear that *we are working with the limb system, not the brain;* foundations are being laid for the life of will, not thinking. The brain must be left as undisturbed as possible while the ego uses growth forces to perfect its physical structure. This is the first fundamental fact.

The second fact, equally crucial, is this; *throughout the first seven years the child's thinking is pictorial.* It is not logical, intellectual or abstract. It could be described as a picture-doing-thinking.[5] It is closely connected with the will, and thereby becomes creative. The child thinks pictorially as he 'does'. The action is not an *outcome* of the thinking; rather, the picture arises in the child's mind during the activity. He does not first conceptualize a plan of action; the thinking works in conjunction with the doing. (Observe and listen to children in sandpit or dolls' corner and this fact will reveal itself). It can be said that the child reasons with his hands not his head.

In this way the child prepares his future. He gains the possibility of developing strong and imaginative forces of soul to sustain him throughout life's journey.

Chapter Thirteen
The First Seven Years

We have seen how the child's body and soul reveal to the perceptive observer rhythms of development extending over seven year periods. Throughout, the ego is active, its work undergoing metamorphosis as each new period emerges. There is not only the physical body to be penetrated and moulded, but life-forces and soul-forces must also be worked upon. The process of incarnation continues.

While each of these seven year periods flow naturally into the next, forming a whole, nevertheless each one has its own special characteristics. We must now consider the first of these in some detail. We will return to the baby.

The Madonna's Cloak

After the baby's birth, not only does the mother's body undergo changes, but also her psychological life. In the latter there is an intensification of feeling, an outpouring of warmth and protectiveness which ripens into a true mother-love. A stirring of heart forces expresses itself in a tenderness and caring, often well-nigh overwhelming.

This outstreaming of the mother's soul can be pictured as forming a protective cloak around the baby – a Madonna's Cloak, raying out into the environment and affecting the whole atmosphere surrounding the child. Within the cloak there are weaving colours, warming, radiant and light-filled, (or perhaps rather dull and murky depending upon the quality of the mother's soul life). For the young child, such a Madonna's cloak is a spiritual reality. It enfolds him in warmth and deeply affects him.

We all too readily imagine that our thoughts and feelings dissipate leaving no trace on the environment. But anyone who can sense the different atmospheres pervading, say a sports centre, a church and a business office, will be very much aware of the lasting effect of our psychological life. It impresses its forces upon the environment, forming itself into a certain atmosphere.

Thus the Madonna's Cloak is more than a fanciful picture. It portrays a reality.[1]

Pursuing this, it can be said that during the early months, and in fact for the first three years, the young child, living within the cloak, experiences himself as part of Mother, sharing fully her soul life. As pointed out previously, he has no experience of his own identity. If Mother's soul life is calm and joyous, so will the baby within the Madonna's Cloak be similarly affected. If Mother is nervous and anxious, this also will be expressed in the cloak. It is an intimate relationship, and each subtle change of mood brings a different nuance of colour and tone.

Father participates too, adding his own individual pattern of colour, his own tone to weave within the cloak's folds. There is a mutual interweaving of soul forces, sometimes surging and stormy, at other times calm and peaceful, colouring the soul environment within which the family lives.

For the young child, a good quality Madonna's Cloak is one of the most important things throughout the first three years. It mitigates the effect of errors of judgement which parents and others may make. In fact, these are of no lasting significance, and in no way damage the child psychologically if the environment is stable and of good quality. Doing the right thing is of course desirable, but even the wrong thing does no harm provided the Madonna's Cloak is full of warmth, light and lovely colours. Within such a spiritual reality, minor errors pale into insignificance.

From the above will be seen the enormous importance of what was discussed in Chapter Four; the mother's inward preparation during pregnancy. The quality of the Madonna's Cloak is prepared during pregnancy as the mother prepares her soul.

At about two years of age the child develops what Rudolf Steiner calls "the feeling of 'I'". We can now envisage the cloak beginning to fold back as the child begins to sense his own separateness and starts to experiment with the word 'I'. Over the next year this leads to "the idea of the 'I'", and the full folding back of the cloak. The child, as it were, steps out into the world recognizing his own identity. He is about three years of age. In a way, he is only now fully born; he stands in the world by himself speaking of himself as 'I'.

The mighty forces of heaven within which he has hitherto been immersed, now relate to him in a different way.[2] A new chapter of his life has begun.

On the physical plane there have been changes too. During these three years there has been a growing maturity of the brain, especially the cerebrum, and the development of medullary sheaths in the cerebral cortex. The brain has become a more efficient instrument able to used more effectively by the ego. A step forward in ego consciousness becomes possible, and the child recognizes himself.

Often children of this age become anxious, wanting a light in their room at night, or demanding to go out with Mother rather than be minded by a friend. This is a temporary stage indicating the child's initial inability to cope with his new position in the world. It will pass, but at the time calls for reassurance and understanding.

Now there is much to learn. This world, full of fascinating things and events which are seen with new eyes, must be fully investigated. It is a challenge taken up with enthusiasm.

Asking Questions

Careful listening to children of three or four years of age gives an insight into their longing to learn about the world. It is the great question-asking time. "Why do the birds fly, Mummy?" "What makes the car go, Daddy?" and "Who lights the stars, Grandma?" The child, looking at the world with his more wide-awake eyes, has an insatiable curiosity. He yearns to know about what he himself now perceives; he is no longer looking through Mother's eyes. His questions go on and on. They need a simple direct answer and not too much detail. He will wholeheartedly *believe* what he is told; for questioning and believing is an early method of learning.

Later he will come to *knowing*, and later still to *understanding*.[3] An overheard conversation between two four year olds reveals this sequence. It went like this . . .

> First child, showing a bean seed:
> "If I plant this seed in the ground and
> water it, a bean plant will grow."
> Second Child: "It will not."
> First Child: "It will so."
> Second Child: "How do you know?"
> First Child: "Because my Dad said so – so there!"

This illuminating conversation points to implicit belief. Dad has said so and that was good enough for him. It is a first step. Knowing will come later as the bean seed does, in fact, become a bean plant; and later still there will be an understanding of the laws of botany. Let it be noted that understanding comes last in this sequence.

There is a lesson for us here. Detailed and reasoned explanations are of little or no value to the young child. He cannot follow their rationale. He looks for a simple answer from a trusted adult, and that he will believe.

Later on, questions about life and death, God and religion are best answered by telling a story, giving the child an imaginative word picture wherein an answer lies. Some old tales such as the story of Mother Holle (Grimm) can be a help here. Much will depend upon the parents' own religious background and convictions.

Imitation and Repetition

Prior to this three year stage, much will have already been learned by imitating the example of others, particularly parents and close family members. It is an enormous responsibility to set an example worthy of imitation. Parental quarrels in front of the child, shouting and a display of temper leave their indelible mark. The young child will copy everything he sees and hears whether it be helpful or harmful. He will long to do what he sees Mother and Dad do, for this to him is right and proper. It is good to allow him to help with household chores – bed making, drying up, cooking and cleaning, etc. A wooden iron and some handkerchiefs to press, his own hammer or garden spade give opportunities to enter into family activities in an imitative way.

But more than this, the child also absorbs attitudes, both positive and negative. He copies manner of speech, how Mother greets Dad, and Dad's greeting to Mother on his return from work; how parents speak of neighbours, the kindergarten teacher and butcher and baker and candlestick maker – all these attitudes flow into the child, leaving an imprint engraved upon his soul. He will carry them well into the future.

Learning by imitation goes on throughout the first seven years. It is helped by repetition, and the child repeats over and over again what he has achieved and what he hears. Once he has mastered a skill he will endlessly practise it; and will want to hear the same bedtime story every night. Repetition stamps the known activity right into his body. Imitating and repeating, questioning and believing – thus the child learns in the early years.

There is also play. It is through his play that the child learns about life; through playing he prepares himself to meet life's future situations.

Play

The child's play is much more than something which keeps him amused. Within play activities there are, at a child's level, the same situations as are met with in later life. There are challenges to be met, problems to be solved when a block building collapses, relationships to be established, materials to be used creatively, and difficult situations which call for innovation and improvisation. There is the whole world of art – painting, singing and dancing; and there are activities and playthings which engage the child's emotions such as listening to stories, a favourite doll or animal to be lovingly nurtured. All of these are life situations in miniature.

The little girl or boy who loves a special doll, caring for it tenderly, singing a lullaby as it is put to bed, is the adult who will be the loving, caring parent, nurse, doctor or welfare worker. The child able to solve challenging situations when, with his fire engine he becomes a rescuing hero, will be the adult able to resolve difficulties in the office, laboratory or factory, and 'rescue' the work situation.

Play prepares the future, and playthings and the play environment should give opportunities for this. This means that playthings should be such as to offer a variety of possibilities; for example, off-cuts of wood that can be used for building, for simple carpentry, can become logs carried on a truck to the sawmill, or even be dressed up to become a doll. Playthings must have a 'do-with' quality; they must be able to be used creatively in a variety of ways, and not be just looked at as they sit decoratively on a shelf.

The baby first plays with his own body. He discovers his hands and often his feet, looks at them in wonder and then puts them into his mouth to explore further. This usually happens at about three months. At four or five months he is able to firmly grasp and retain objects, and this is a good time for a rattle. It should be artistic and preferably spherical in shape, for this is the cosmic form we see in sun, moon and dome of the sky. The child feels a natural connection with it.[4] Wood is preferable to plastic, and if a special friend offers to give a very special present a small silver bell is a wonderful gift. Its beautiful tone delights and brings harmony to the child's soul.

Early in the second year the child is ready for a doll. This is an important toy and we will consider it in some detail.

The first doll should be of cloth in a carefully chosen colour – pink, blue, light mauve or yellow – be soft enough to cuddle and not be too finished. Features such as nose and mouth are not necessary; it is sufficient that the human form be shown. This allows the child's imaginative forces full play. A doll with eye lashes, a stylish hair-do etc., one which even wets its nappie, leaves nothing to imagine. It is a finished product, and however cleverly designed it may be, it has not the same power to promote the child's fantasy as has a more primitive doll. When the child is older, say about three to four years, hair and eyes can be added and nose and mouth indicated. The head can then be carefully moulded to a sphere. Doll making is a wonderful art, and most Rudolf Steiner schools have classes where parents can learn this truly rewarding activity. For to make a doll for one's own child, to design and mould it so it is just suited in form and colour for that special individual, is a truly creative act.

As the child grows, the doll will become a friend to be talked to, told secrets, taken for outings and so on. It is a first step in developing later friendships. Or the doll may be a baby who has to be fed, have her nappie changed, treated with loving care, nurtured when sick, and tenderly mothered or fathered. Again, it is a first step in a later caring for one's own children.

It is important that parents respect the child's devotion to a favourite doll, for to the child this doll is really one of the family. Often the child will imbue it with her or his own soul qualities, or with those of a close member of the family. It takes on a real personality and must be treated as such.

Three or four dolls is an adequate number. If the child is given too many and feels cluttered, it is almost impossible for him to form a real relationship with each one – to truly love the doll. This applies not only to dolls but to all toys. Most children in our affluent society have far too many toys, and thus often become blasé about them all, not feeling a real connection with any; or, on the other hand, selecting one favourite toy and ignoring all the rest. In the former case there is no soul involvement for the child, and in the latter it is a sheer waste of money! Of how much greater value is it for the child if he has a few good-quality well-loved toys for which he truly cares.

Once he is able to walk, the child can be given wooden or soft fabric animals. Hand-knitted lambs, horses, ducks etc., stuffed with pure wool are great favourites. (See Appendix M for "How to knit a pony".) In their form they should accurately indicate the real animal and not be a caricature such as 'Mickey Mouse'. While the child is striving to be upright, but not yet able to maintain the vertical, dolls (which are human in form) are preferable to the horizontal animal. As already indicated, a toy in a child's eyes, takes on a soul quality, and indeed, those people who make dolls affirm this too. Each doll has its own personality, as also does this little furry rabbit and the strong wooden horse. It is hardly necessary to say that all toys should be artistic in form and colour.

When the child is reasonably firm on his feet, he will love to push long-handled carts, pull along wooden animals on wheels, and chase moving balls. This encourages limb activity, and as we have seen, the limbs are the bodily organs of will. It will be recalled that throughout the first seven years we are working with the early development of will forces. Certainly, thinking and emotion are there too, but it is not yet their time for full development. (For a discussion of development of thinking, see Chapter Sixteen.)

Between the first and second years, the child will most likely go through a stage of building-up and breaking-down, of putting-in and throwing-out. He builds a tower with blocks then pushes it down; he throws everything out of his cot, and immediately Mother gives them back he throws them out again; or he gathers everything into a basket, and throws them out. It is an early version of hide and seek. Through this form of play we see an expression of the child's soul 'throwing' itself out into the world, then gathering itself together and penetrating deeply into the body. It also mirrors the child's experience of body processes, the building up and breaking down of matter within his organism.[5] It is a natural developmental stage, and does not indicate that the child is becoming destructive.

During the pre-school years, as thinking becomes more pictorial and will forces find expression, play becomes creative. Now group activities emerge, and the 'alongside' play of the earlier years gives way to a doing-things-together stage. Here a variety of natural materials can be used in a creative way. Gum nuts, acorns, twigs, shells, flowers, stones, leaves, grasses, cotton reels, a variety of fabrics ad infinitum are ideal for decorating the house built from cartons, or simply making into an artistic display on a low table.

Other favourites are Mother's and Dad's discarded shoes, handbags and clothes. Dressing up always fascinates a child unspoilt by our technical age. Large pieces of coloured cloth or old sheets and towels to drape over large cartons, small tables, or upturned kitchen chairs are excellent material for making cubby houses. We have seen in Chapter Nine what this stage signifies. Much can be achieved in the home with virtually no expense, and a garden with uncultivated bushy areas gives limitless opportunities.

Very different is the clutter of unimaginative (usually plastic!) toys inflicted on many of today's children. Such toys may fascinate for a while, but a truly creative child will soon tire of them. This is the experience of perceptive parents and kindergarten teachers.

Activities which give scope for limb activity can be fostered at this age. A good quality carpenter's set which won't break as soon as it is used, or one good quality hammer are of great value. The child should be shown how to use them and take care of them, putting them away in their own place after use. The child who has learned to care for his toys is the man who will care for the world. Wheelbarrows, dolls' pram or cradle etc. have a real place in encouraging a variety of play activities, and a sand-pit offers unlimited scope.

Painting, singing, dancing, weaving a simple woollen mat, modelling, listening to a story, and as mentioned earlier doing eurythmy, all introduce an artistic element, so vital for today's child. We have dealt with this when discussing the development of the senses. An artistic element is imperative for children if they are to overcome much that is destructive in their environment. Fortunate indeed is the child whose life from the earliest years is enriched by eurythmy, music and art. He or she will be the well-balanced and successful individual of tomorrow.

Simple action games belong to the pre-school age of about 3½ years onwards. They can be played within the family or by a group of friends on special occasions. Mother or Dad speaks the words and everyone participates in the action. We include only two here, but there are many more within this repertoire.

Footsteps

The foxes move so softly that we do not hear a sound.
The trotting horse's hoof beats ring out loudly on the ground.
And little lambs in springtime gaily skip around.

The children will love moving softly on tip toe, trotting and gaily skipping about.

Spiral

To be led by a parent or older child.

> Let us make a little visit to the curly house of snail
> Round we go until we find him hidden in his coat of mail;
> Then we turn and go back homeward still awinding all the way,
> Till we come out of his tunnel to the sunny light of day.
>
> Molly de Havas

Many of the nursery rhymes make excellent action games for this age – for instance, "Oranges and Lemons", "Twinkle Twinkle Little Star", and "Cobbler Cobbler Mend my Shoe."

It is a sad fact that many children today are not able to truly play. They lack initiative and imagination. There are three main reasons for this. First is television watching which, as we have seen, induces passivity and cripples initiative. Second, many modern playthings lack an 'open-ended' quality, and therefore cannot be used imaginatively. Barbie dolls and Fisher Price boards could be cited as examples of this. The third reason for a child's inability to initiate play out of himself is the misguided idea of some parents that the child needs to be constantly provided with new and stimulating things to do, and constantly entertained and played with. This applies particularly to first or only children. The question "What can I do now Mummy?" is a telling commentary on this phenomenon.

But let us end this section on a positive note. All children long to have play opportunities wherein they can express their rapidly-burgeoning creative powers.

If parents understand this and what it implies in choice of playthings, then much can be done in the home even within the most limited circumstances. It is a matter of parents themselves being imaginative and recognizing the child's real needs.

We have devoted a good deal of space to this vital activity of play. Much more could be said about it, but hopefully its great importance and long-term significance have been sufficiently indicated.

Books

From books we can learn much about the world, but more than this, they can become our companions along life's journey. We gain ideas, our feelings are stirred and our soul often uplifted. Fortunate is he who finds just the right book at a moment of inner need. He treasures this as a precious gift, and values it all his life. To introduce the child to books can lead to these attitudes provided the parents set such an example. Books must become well cared-for friends, to be cherished and treated with respect. Thus can the child be helped to later find the treasures of literature and gain sustenance for his soul.

The choice of books for children is such a vast subject that only the barest guidelines can be given here. As a general principle, it goes without saying that artistry should be a key-note of picture books, and as in the case of toys, people and animals should be portrayed in a way which resembles their true form. A duck should be recognizable as a duck; a dog look like a dog; a king should be regal and dignified; a man be a true representative of humanity. The deplorable *Mr Men* series is a sorry and degrading portrayal of everything human. It can only undermine a child's respect for what should be the dignity of man.

It is difficult to discuss pictures without having examples in front of one. But if we imagine illustrations that draw our eyes in so that they feel around the picture like a pair of hands would feel a texture, then there is an active looking. In contrast to this, there are illustrations that leap out at one, that push the viewer into himself, so that only a passive looking is possible. The latter offer nothing that the child can enter into in an active way. If we work with this idea and practise it, some pictures will begin to speak to our eyes, and we will know which books to choose.

For the toddler, pictures of familiar objects and animals make a good beginning. Later, a nursery rhyme book simply illustrated, will become a great favourite. As the child becomes older, simple stories can be introduced. There can be tales of Nature such as the thirsty tree that was overjoyed when given water; or the sleepy grub that turned into a beautiful butterfly. Books showing people and familiar events – going to the Zoo with Grandpa – and imaginative stories of animals are also suitable for this age group. Special books such as those telling the timeless Christmas story can become special treasures.

To be avoided at all cost are books designed to educate – for example, "What shape is it?" and "What size is it?" This type of book presents concepts which have no reality for the child – the triangle, the square, mass and so on. They neither fire his imagination nor engage his fantasy. For the child they present what is only deadly dull meaningless information.

By contrast, it is the old fairy tales, particularly those collected by the Grimm brothers that really speak to the child. We will now consider the tremendous wisdom to be found in these old stories.[6] They come from far-off times.

Fairy Tales

It has already been pointed out (see Chapter Seven) that in their bodily development children are a mirror-image of past stages of evolution. This fundamental principle of macrocosmic processes expressing themselves microcosmically, also applies to the child's growth of consciousness. Prior to the birth of the intellect, and particularly in the pre-school years, a child could be described as being dreamy in his consciousness; and in so far as this is so, he lives in an inner condition similar to that of the whole of humanity of past ages. In those bygone days the common people received from the wise men truths of life in the form of fairy tale images. It could be said that this fairy tale teaching was their only form of education. Then there were no schools for the common man whose dreamy consciousness, very different from our own wide-awake mind, had not evolved sufficiently to be educated in the modern sense.

It is for the brief span of years during which children live in this same dreamy state of consciousness (or perhaps one must say today, should be allowed to live in it!) that fairy stories with their wonderful imagery are the 'education' par excellence. Their wisdom and morality speak to the child of the reality of a world of spirit, a world of which, as we have seen, he is very much aware. For the pictures contained in fairy stories are not allegorical or symbolic, they portray images of spiritual realities that help the child grasp moral concepts and truths in a pictorial way.

The beautiful Princess and handsome Prince (or, one could say, the pure soul and higher self) living happily ever after, and the wicked witch meeting a just punishment are much more real to a child than a lengthy rational explanation of moral behaviour. A child who is allowed to live in these images will be helped to a true conceptual thinking in later life, "for there is a straight path which leads of itself from these true pictures to the true concepts of later years."[7]

It is a great temptation to explore many of these old tales to gain a greater understanding of their ineffable treasure; but we will look just briefly at one which is well known, The Sleeping Beauty. Ursula Grahl, in her book *The Wisdom in Fairy Tales*, illuminates it with penetrating insight.

The story speaks of twelve Good Fairies who bestow wonderful gifts and blessings upon the newborn princess; and a thirteenth fairy who introduces dangers and difficulties which will confront the princess later on. We have here a picture of both the heavenly and earthly realms. The twelve good fairies eat from golden plates, and have the power to bestow life-long blessing, while the thirteenth carries the sting of death. Each newborn child is in this situation. As we have seen, he has come from the heavenly world, and must now face earth's thorns and dangers.

In Chapter Twelve we spoke of the birth of the intellect at puberty and described it as that type of thinking which gives us information of all that is sense perceptible. Later on we will look at its strengths and limitations and will see its inability to give knowledge of anything beyond the material. If we relied on our intellect alone, we would be asleep to the reality of spirit. (See Chapter Fifteen.)

In the fairy tale, the princess at puberty (age 15) pricks her finger on a spindle and she and the whole castle fall asleep. This takes place in a small room at the top of the tower. Her childhood consciousness which kept her in touch with the good fairies vanishes and she is asleep to the heavenly realities.

What could be a clearer picture of the birth of the intellect, that sort of thinking which takes place in the "small room at the top of the tower" – our brain – and which, as we shall see, needs a higher soul faculty to illuminate it. Here we have the secret of the story. For it is when the Prince (the higher self, carrying knowledge of the spirit) kisses the sleeping Princess (the soul) that she awakens and is restored to her former heavenly state. One could say, her thinking soul capacity has been enlightened and expanded to grasp the higher reality. (See Chapter Fifteen.)

Ursula Grahl expresses it thus: "Only when our higher self awakens to new spiritual perception, only when the true prince approaches the hedge do the thorns recede and, shining through the blossoms, there appears again the enchanted castle of our childhood. When the spirit has kissed the soul into a new awakeness, then the whole castle comes to life again. Heaven and earth are once more united . . . and the soul and spirit of man are once again in the home of their cosmic childhood."[8]

Similar profundities are contained in all Grimm's fairy tales. They are a veritable treasure-chest of wisdom.

Tales suitable for the pre-school years are, Cinderella, The Frog Prince, Sweet Porridge, Mother Holle, Goldilocks, Snow White and Rose Red, The Sleeping Beauty, Snow White and the Seven Dwarfs, Tom Thumb, Beauty and the Beast and others. They can be shown in puppetry or told. Then there must be a special fairy tale atmosphere created by Mother or Dad; a quietness, a mood of reverence, a lighted candle – a magic pervading the room. An unspoilt child will enter into this fairy tale magic mood and his soul will be at peace.

Telling the story in this way just before bed time will often help a restless, wakeful child to sleep soundly. This has been reported by a number of mothers attending the Gabriel Centre.

Children love to hear the same story over and over again, so that the characters become real friends; and this is enhanced if parents can tell the story rather than read it. The child will feel more at home with a familiar story than with a new one every night. Parents need to be very familiar with the tale, so they can use as much of the original language as possible.

Fairy stories should begin and end in the right way, and the content should not be altered.[9] "Once upon a time" and "they lived happily ever after" are an intrinsic part of the tale, and modern versions which omit parts and add others will very likely fail in their purpose.

This is an almost inexhaustible subject. Only a glimpse can be given here. To those wishing to gain deeper insight into this fount of wisdom is recommended Ursula Grahl's small book.

The World of Gnomes and Fairies.

A child brought up in the way here advocated, familiar with the fairy stories we have been discussing and living within the richness of their content, will be familiar with the realm of fairies, gnomes, elves and other such beings. There are various ways that parents can bring something of this world to the child. Stories, puppetry, an especially-prepared eurythmy and simple plays all help the child enter into this realm.

Down the ages, ancient knowledge of an elemental world expressed itself in images which we, with our prosaic outlook, regard as either romantic or totally fantastic. Our souls have long since lost touch with much that the child experiences; for constant demands on time and attention leave their mark on our inner life as we become more and more immersed in the daily round.

In many children today, this ancient knowledge is again expressing itself in soul pictures of which the child speaks quite naturally and matter-of-factly. Such a child, and in fact all children, will benefit greatly from stories such as the 'Tomten' series by Astrid Lindgren, 'Snow White and the Seven Dwarfs', or for the older child, a wondrous tale called 'The Princess and the Goblin' by George MacDonald. If eurythmy, puppetry and plays are added to the stories, parents and teachers will have bestowed a priceless gift.

Nursery Rhymes

Before leaving this area of books and stories, let us look briefly at nursery rhymes. They are universal and have been sung and spoken by mothers and grandmothers for countless generations. They are different from fairy tales, often quite trivial, yet always enchanting. Walter de la Mare says of them, "Many of them are masterpieces of word craftsmanship . . . they are not only crammed with vivid little scenes and objects and living creatures, but however fantastic and nonsensical they may be, they are a direct short-cut into poetry itself."[10]

Yet some of them do seem to speak at a deeper level. For example the "pussy-cat that went to London to see the Queen," and only chased the little mouse under the chair is one such rhyme. Perhaps it indicates that we see only what our eyes are capable of seeing. We will never see the Queen, but only chase the little mouse unless we develop our seeing capacity. One is reminded here of what was said about eyes that see in Chapter Eleven.

In "Mary Had a Little Lamb", a meaning emerges in the last verse –

Why does the lamb love Mary so?
The eager children cry;
Why, Mary loves the lamb you know,
The teacher did reply.

For this reason it is good to have a nursery rhyme book in which all the verses are given. Like fairy tales, nursery rhymes for the pre-school years are often frowned upon by many of today's child educators. Certainly, the "cow jumping over the moon" may not make sense to our clever intellects, but children delight in its rhythm and imagery.

The nursery rhyme age starts at about fifteen months, continues into the pre-school years, and with many children, even into the early school years up to Class 2. Rhymes associated with rhythmic games are especially suitable during the primary school years up to approximately age nine. Some popular ones are "I had a little nut tree", "Here we go round the mulberry bush", and "London bridge is falling down".

All children love to hear the rhymes sung and soon learn the words themselves. Their rhythm and the pictures they evoke are in harmony with the sleepy-dreamy consciousness of the early years.

Like the fairy tales, nursery rhymes are the exact opposite of educational books. They speak not to the head but to the knowing heart, and as such they are the birthright of every child.

Festivals

People of olden days celebrated special occasions by holding a festival. These were usually related to cycles of the season such as a harvest festival, to cosmic events such as the winter and summer solstices, or to the special religious occasions such as Whitsun, Easter and Christmas.

To give children an opportunity to experience these special times brings them into contact with the rhythm of the seasons and the deeper mysteries of life. Families who celebrate these festivals in their home, who find a special ceremony to suit the occasion and perhaps a special poem, song, or simple dance, and who with the help of the children prepare a special meal, these families bring an abundance of riches to all who participate and especially to children.

One such family has written of their winter solstice celebration as follows:[11]

"At midwinter the sun is fully descended and we have our shortest day. It is also the point from which our days grow longer, so at the point of the greatest darkness we have a festival to celebrate the coming of the Light – the rebirth of the sun, so to speak.

We made our winter solstice celebration a festival of light. Before the solstice there was candle dipping, lantern making, walks in the garden, park and bush to gather 'winter' (bare twigs, leaves, lichen, mossy rocks, pods, flowers – whatever there was). We made a special table and centre-piece with these, and put a large candle in the middle – wattle blossoms massed around the candle looked wonderful. We brought in a special pot with bulbs, leaves just appearing, and a tree decorated with candles, bright yellow balls and yellow flowers.

On the morning of the solstice, we lit the candle and let it burn all day; and in the evening we had a special meal. We had prepared this ahead of time with the children helping as much as possible. First there was a golden pumpkin soup with seedy crusty rolls, and then pumpkin pie followed by orange cake made rich with eggs, honey and dried fruit. We set the table with a bright yellow cloth, and had a large bowl of oranges as well.

As evening came, we sat quietly together at the table and felt darkness closing in. We ate our meal by candle and lantern light and let our 'golden food' become light within. While gathered around the table, we told the children a winter folk tale, telling of the coming of the Light.

Then we all rugged up and went for a walk in the night with our candles and lanterns. We felt the chill, and the dark, and the stars as we experienced the shortest day and the longest night.".

Within the Family Circle

> "Family life is of pre-eminent importance
> . . . 'there is no place like home'."
> John Bowlby

So wrote the eminent child psychiatrist John Bowlby over thirty years ago.[12] Does his statement still hold good today? – and if so, what does the preservation of family life entail for today's parents? Does the creation of a family circle mean that Mother has to totally sacrifice her own individuality and become only 'Mum'?

The family circle is a living organism which evolves and adapts as the consciousness of humanity evolves. It does not remain static and impose itself with a set of fixed rules upon any generation. Rather, it grows anew according to the consciousness of those who re-create it. The tight restrictive family circle of Victorian days of course has no place in today's world; but does this mean that the baby of one or two months old is just as well-off in a crèche while mother pursues her career, convincing herself that the child will be well cared-for and will receive adequate mothering during evenings and weekends?

What has already been stated gives the answer to this question, for everything discussed in this chapter pre-supposes family life. The Madonna's Cloak, parental example, answering the child's questions, the celebration of festivals, singing nursery rhymes together, and telling the fairy stories in a special way, all of these need a family setting if they are to give of their full bounty. Even play, which of course goes on at the crèche or pre-school centre, needs its roots in the early play experiences gained at home. Play at three years of age cannot suddenly blossom out of nothing, or from the aridity of a soul denied from the earliest weeks the fullness of family life.

Yet, there is the mother who, out of sheer economic necessity must go to work. What of her children? Here we must consider the best age at which to leave the child, and the type of care provided. If economically possible, it is of far-reaching benefit to a child to live within a stable family for at least the first three years however devoid the home may be of material comforts. It is the quality of what has been called the Madonna's Cloak – that is, the atmosphere pervading the home – which is the important thing for the child, and this does not depend on the things which money buys.

Once the child goes to kindergarten, a part-time job is often possible. But should necessity force a mother to work full time earlier than this, then the best minding situation for baby or toddler is within the family of a familiar friend. This is infinitely less disturbing than even the very best crèche.[13] To be most strenuously avoided is the situation where the child is minded by Grandma on Monday and Tuesday, Aunt Jane on Wednesday, goes to the crèche on Thursday and is cared for by a neighbour on Friday. This child is the future adult unable to establish or maintain stable relationships, who suffers from feelings of isolation, of not belonging anywhere. There has been a lack of constancy during the formative years.

In discussing causes of mental ill-health, Bowlby has this to say:

"Among the most significant developments of psychiatry during the first quarter of a century has been the steady growth of evidence that the quality of the parental care which a child receives in his earliest years is of vital importance for his future mental health . . . It is this complex, rich, and rewarding relationship with mother in early years, varied in countless ways by relations with the father and with brothers and sisters, that child psychiatrists and many others now believe to underlie the development of character and of mental health."[14]

Of course all mothers need a day off now and then – a free day restores tired bodies and flagging spirits. A good arrangement which meets this need is to share minding with a trusted friend; to alternate weeks so that each has a day off once a fortnight. Once children are about two years of age they can tolerate this quite well – and Mother has the thrill of planning ahead for a gloriously free day!

But sadly, there is the broken circle – often the shattered circle – and we must also consider this. How are these children affected?

There is an enormous literature on this subject, and innumerable studies have been done on all aspects of divorce, broken marriages, new partners and so on.[15]

It seems that "pre-school children are the most distressed at the time of marital rupture . . . (but) they emerge less consciously troubled than their older siblings . . . Children who are very young are considerably less burdened in the years to come than those who were older at the time of divorce."[16]

Authorities agree that if children can remain in the home after marriage breakdown, and if home life can be restored, these children eventually adjust well.

" . . . Children do well in harmonious warm families whether they be one parent, two-parent or step-family . . . Most accept the situation and adjust with the passage of time – but it is not easy for the first twelve months to two years."[17]

Judith Wallerstein who interviewed children five and then ten years after parental separation found "a strong connection between adequate psychological adjustment in children, and overall quality of life within the post-divorce or remarried family". Also, "most of the young people look forward optimistically to marriage and a family".[18] It would seem that while they are disturbed, most are not permanently damaged.

These studies and many others confirm what Bowlby found over thirty years ago; namely, that for the child, the crucial thing is the quality of life in the home. Whether this be with Mother or Father only, or with either parent and a new partner, is less relevant than the warmth of heart and loving care pervading 'home sweet home'. Truly, for the child there is no place like home.

What we have been discussing does not imply that mothers should feel confined to the 'drudgery' of home life with its day-to-day chores and demands. Far from it! Today's family circle is not a closed sphere; it breathes freely, and is not restrictive. There are doors and windows leading to the outside world. It accommodates free days for Mother, parental outside interests, often a part-time job for mother once the children are older and established at school. The essential criterion is that the home remains a focal point. The family circle can indeed be fertilized and enriched by what flows into it from outside, and what it has the strength and stability to assimilate – or, dare one say, redeem.

Within such a family circle there is the possibility of finding 'I am' in family life, of recognizing, 'you are', and of achieving 'we are' which, blossoming like a lovely flower, spreads its colour and perfume in ever-widening circles.

To achieve a true family circle today takes perseverance, usually sacrifice, a recognition of the other, and sheer hard work. The path is often full of boulders, landslides, and thorny bushes; but for those who have struggled through, the rewards are manifold. These families are like an oasis in a barren land.[19] They bring succour and refreshment to our battered society, and are always a joy to behold.

Chapter Fourteen
Questions and Viewpoints

At the very beginning, in Chapter One, we discussed the difference between the old instinctive art of motherhood and that which superseded it, the science of child rearing. The former expressed itself in a confident caring for the child, while from the latter many questions and uncertainties have emerged. Parents today are concerned about their child's social development, discipline, whether to let the baby cry or not, decisions about immunization, whether the toddler should attend a crêche regularly to be socially stimulated, play-groups for toddlers, how the child can be encouraged to be a caring person and so on. All these things are of real concern to many parents today. They are serious questions, important for parents and children alike. We will explore some of them in an endeavour to find a path through their maze. As is our usual practice, the baby will be our starting point.

Crying

One of the things which most affects the hearts of parents, and especially mothers, is the baby's crying. This is particularly so in the case of a first child. The little one seems in great distress, tears rolling down cheeks, yet everything possible has been done to comfort him; he has been fed, nappie changed, burped, rocked and so on.

"Will he be psychologically damaged if allowed to cry?" That is the burning question for parents, especially in the middle of the night after Mother has been up two or three times already and can hardly drag herself out of bed yet another time.

We will approach this question by first looking at adult grief and then comparing it with the distress of a crying infant.

Adult grief can penetrate deep into the soul. A dearly beloved one is killed, an older child turns to crime, and parents are literally wracked with grief; they feel saddened to the core of their being. If prolonged, this may even go so far as to affect the body. The face takes on a sorrowful expression, and we hear of people whose whole body is 'bowed with grief'. To laugh and be merry, to celebrate and be full of fun would be unthinkable and quite impossible. The sadness sinks into the deepest recesses of the soul and frequently leaves deep furrows, indelibly marked. Often these are impossible to erase and can only be overlaid.

Even a lesser sadness, not an intense grief, affects the adult soul, and very likely there will be tears and unhappiness, and a feeling of misery for days or weeks on end. In this state, laughter and merriment have no place.

Let us now compare this with the baby's apparent distress when crying. He may not want to be put to bed, may have tummy ache, or be overtired. Whatever the cause, he cries and seems thoroughly unhappy. Mother picks him up, and in a matter of seconds he is all smiles again, gurgling and cooing with happiness. Gone is the distress and he is restored to his usual cheerful smiling self.

It is very obvious that his soul has hardly been touched by his crying. There has been no deep penetration of a lasting nature. In the infant, the effects of crying are like faint pencil marks on the surface of the soul, and can easily be erased; they leave no mark whatever. Only very severe and traumatic experiences sink beneath the surface and may leave a mark. One can think of the so-called 'battered baby' and other such disasters. Fortunately these are not usual occurrences.

A healthy infant is not psychologically damaged by a 'normal' amount of crying. On the physical level it gives an opportunity to fully inhale and exhale, to aerate the lungs, and from this point of view may even be beneficial. Dr D. W. Winnicott, a child psychiatrist in the U.K., has this to say: "Doctors say that the lusty cry of the new-born infant is a sign of health and strength. Well, crying goes on being a sign of health and strength, an early form of P.T., an exercise of a function . . ."[1] However, if an infant persistently cries, it is important that medical advice be sought.

It is the wakeful baby who cries frequently at night that causes parents most concern. Such a lot has been written about night waking[2] that it is not proposed to discuss it in any detail here. A few suggestions only will be given.

As a first step, the infant needs to be firmly wrapped when put down to sleep. (See Chapter Six.) Professor Jolly also advocates this. He points out that "It is usual for a baby to be wrapped up securely in the first month before being put in his cot to sleep".[3] The second step is to try to remain calm oneself. It is best not to lift an older child out of the cot. His nappie, if wet, can be changed in the cot, and Mother or Dad caress him without lifting him out. Speaking to him calmly and softly often helps. It is a great mistake to carry a wakeful baby about for hours in the middle of the night. If he persists in crying, and is in good health, he can be left to it for periods, with Mother or Dad returning at regular intervals to reassure him. Certainly, he should not feel abandoned altogether! Most healthy babies will respond to this regime eventually although it may take two or three weeks.

However, during the first six weeks of baby's life, often a few weeks longer depending on the child, the best policy in the night is to breast feed whenever the baby wants it. Most infants will then return to sleep for a further three or four hours. If the child remains wakeful and restless, it is often a help for Mother to take him into her own bed. Almost every baby will sleep if cuddled up close to Mother. From about three months of age onwards, a more rhythmic pattern of feeding can be encouraged, and this includes night feeding. The reader is reminded of what was said about the importance of rhythm in nutrition in Appendix H. One breast feed in the middle of the night is a usual and acceptable practice for many mothers during the first six months. After that it is best discouraged, and the regime suggested above for older children can be tried. Even if the child is a night-owl, mother needs a good night's rest! Let parents rest assured that a reasonable amount of crying causes no psychological damage.

Laughing and crying are part of life. They both have a place in the scheme of things.

Immunization

Today, many parents are questioning the wisdom of introducing such a foreign substance as a vaccine into the baby's organism at two months of age. They are conscious that the infant's body is designed only for the mother's milk.

Yet there is the spectre of diphtheria, whooping cough and poliomyelitis, and the fear associated with these. Some parents are anxious that the baby will be exposed to untold harm if denied protection against such potentially damaging diseases. Added to this there is the attitude of some professionals who often advise parents that not to immunize is irresponsible not only for the baby but also for society as a whole. All of this adds up to a confusing and anxiety-causing situation for many young parents, so vulnerable in the baby's early life.

Let it be said at the outset that the decision whether or not to immunize can only be a parental one. The role of the professional is to inform on *all* aspects of the matter – that is, the dangers associated with having immunization and those of not having it; then to offer advice if requested. There should be no pressure either way. Decisions relating to the well-being of the child are the responsibility of parents alone. Here the *feelings* of the parents must be taken seriously. (See Carl Jung's comment on feelings in Chapter Ten.)

Immunization stimulates the immune system to make antibodies which, it is claimed, will subsequently fight off any invasion of the body by similar bacteria or toxins. This is an artificial process, and one questions whether the degree of immunity it gives is as permanent as that gained by the child fighting the disease himself. There is mounting evidence to show that it does not.[4] One must also ask, "What long-term effect does this artificial stimulation have on the immune system?" In view of today's increasing breakdown of immune systems, this is a highly relevant question. We may also ask, "Where does the primal origin of this breakdown lie? Could it be in the very early months of infancy?" To find an answer to these questions will most likely take many years of research.

However, this is only one aspect. There are a number of other questions to be considered such as why it is that in an epidemic (say, measles), one child will develop the disease and another will not; and why one will have a severe attack with following complications, and another be only mildly affected. Here we are concerned with human factors and many of the things we have discussed in this book. We could ask how the child has been fed, how dressed in cold weather, what sense-impressions he has received and what sort of family atmosphere does he live within. We have seen what an enormous difference all these factors make to the building up of a strong healthy and resistant body organism. There are also questions which affect the child's own individuality. Disease is related to all these things, not only to disease-causing micro-organisms. Informed parents are the best ones to accurately assess these factors.

Furthermore, it is a well-established fact that the whooping cough vaccine contained in Triple Antigen (referred to in some countries as D.P.T.) often causes reactions of varying severity, and in extreme but rare cases severe brain damage.[5] On 17th June 1977, *The Age* newspaper in Melbourne published an article on this matter. A few extracts will suffice to show its theme.

"After a year long battle, the British Government has agreed to pay damages to several hundred children who have suffered brain damage after vaccination. At least 600 children believed to have been damaged by reaction to vaccine will be assessed by a special Government medical unit. Many of the children have been left paralysed or with a mental age of two year olds." The article reports that an Association of Parents of Vaccine Damaged Children had been formed and "has 356 children on its books, about two thirds of whom suffered brain damage after receiving Triple Antigen vaccination."

It may be relevant to mention that the manufacturers of Triple Antigen in Australia (the Commonwealth Serum Laboratories) make a vaccine which conforms to the British Pharmacopoeia.[6] This may not necessarily be identical to that manufactured in the U.K. but no doubt the formula would be basically similar.

In Australia Dr Archie Kalokerinos found other devastating results and a high mortality rate amongst aboriginal children given Triple Antigen.[7]

Even more disturbing is the "possibility that they (the vaccines) act in some other way than by producing a genuine immunity. (This) is suggested by the fact that the diseases in question have continued to break out in highly immunized populations . . . the vaccines do not act merely by producing pale or mild copies of the original disease; all of them also commonly produce a variety of symptoms of their own."[8]

That the vaccines have certain dangers is indicated by their manufacturers. In Australia the Commonwealth Serum Laboratories lists the following 'precautions':

Triple Antigen should not be given if there is any acute illness. It should be replaced by C.D.T. vaccine in children with:

1. a previous history of neurological disease including seizures, convulsions or cerebral irritation in the neo-natal period;
2. a previous reaction to the vaccine other than local minor reactions and/or mild fever; or
3. a family history of neurological disease other than that due to trauma and infections.

There are also a number of contra-indications to giving measles and mumps vaccines, and several 'precautions' are advised. One of these is, "Adrenaline should be available for immediate use in case an anaphylactoid reaction occurs".

Added to the above is the fact that statistics show that the mortality rate from these childhood diseases is virtually nil;[9] and, "for well over the past 10 years, the mortality rate for those infants admitted to the Royal Children's Hospital (Melbourne) with pertussis (whooping cough) has been zero".[10]

It is this information as well as the case for immunization which should be presented to parents if they are to be in a position to make a responsible decision. Such a decision should then be respected by all people.

Certainly, there is a case for having immunization. Poliomyelitis can be a crippling disease, and in such a case the patient is left with physical disabilities throughout life. Likewise diphtheria can have severe and far-reaching complications; and a severe dose of measles can lead to encephalitis. The point being made in this book is that immunization also has well-documented and equally great dangers. These can occur immediately after the injection (e.g. anaphylactic collapse – rare), soon afterwards (brain damage), or may not become apparent until years later.[11] In view of this, both sides of the case should be presented to parents. Unfortunately, this is not the usual practice.

Mention must also be made of another aspect. We must ask if sickness confers any benefit on children other than permanent immunity. This is difficult to assess; yet, perceptive parents often notice a marked change in their children after childhood disease – for example measles or mumps. A child weak in will and rather pale and withdrawn may emerge from such a disease with greater inner strength, enhanced vitality and better all-round health. It is the experience of the disease process and the struggle to overcome the sickness that is strengthening to the soul. This could be of great benefit to the child's destiny well into the future. Anyone whose outlook is limited to the physical will have no understanding of this. Vaccines deny the child this experience and so the chance of significant development is lost. Therefore the vaccine does not confer a true 'good health', but rather, prevents its development.

Next in this discussion, we must consider the best time for immunization for the children of those parents who have made an informed decision to have it.

We have already discussed how the brain, so immature at first, grows very rapidly during the first year. This is clearly seen on the graph of the child's head circumference chart shown in Appendix L. It will readily be seen that at about eighteen months of age the rate of growth slackens and by two years the graph line begins to become almost horizontal. By this stage, the main thrust of growth in the brain and nervous system has taken place, and after three years, growth is minimal.

It would seem highly undesirable to introduce anything into the child's organism which, even in a slight way, may interfere with this amazing growth of the brain organization, particularly a vaccine known to be associated with neurological disorders. Nothing is scientifically known of the *long-term* effects of even slight reactions which many children have after being given Triple Antigen.

Therefore, taking the brain growth as a yardstick, it can be said that about eighteen months seems a desirable age to start. However, if parents are really confident that their child has had an optimum quality upbringing on all levels, then they may prefer to wait until three years. We have already discussed how at this age the child faces the world in a new and more independent way.

Whatever age is chosen, it is most important that the child should be well at the time and have been free of any infection for at least a week prior to the injection being given. Even a slight cold is a contraindication.

It is not proposed here to discuss all the various childhood diseases or particular vaccines in any detail; we will look only at tetanus.

This is not a true childhood disease such as measles, mumps or chickenpox. It is caused by an anaerobic spore-bearing bacillus which lives in the soil. This gains access to the body most often through deep puncture wounds contaminated with soil, but occasionally through an insect bite or even a scratch. Children who live in the country are particularly vulnerable, for animal manure harbours the spores.

Tetanus is a dramatic and extremely painful disease, and often fatal. Therefore it would seem wise that children be given this vaccine. Tetanus vaccine can be given on its own, combined with diphtheria (C.D.T.) or in Triple Antigen. The toxoid on its own (Tetanus Vaccine Adsorbed) is perfectly safe, and the manufacturers list no precautions except that the container should be thoroughly shaken before use. Its side-effects are minimal. The full primary course consists of two injections given six to twelve weeks apart, and a re-inforcing (booster) dose is recommended six to twelve months after the second dose. Further booster doses can be given at ten to twenty year intervals if desired. Similarly, side effects of C.D.T. are minimal, and precautionary measures suggested are the same as for tetanus vaccine.[12]

Homeopathic treatment for an unimmunized person who has sustained a wound, assumes that such treatment will be readily available and within easy reach. If the wound occurs while out trekking in a remote area, this would be highly unlikely. Immunization against tetanus gives a sure and safe immunity.

Finally, in the face of all we do know of the effects of vaccines, and, more important, of all we *don't* know, surely it is wise to be cautious. Parents who decide to have their children immunized should provide the doctor with a written account of any childhood and family illnesses, particularly neurological disorders. Only when the doctor has satisfied him or herself of the safety of the vaccine for this particular child, should parents authorize the injection or dose to be given. To say that this would be too cumbersome in mass immunization programmes, brings into question the advisability of such programmes.

The right way to approach childhood diseases is not to subject every child to the dangers associated with immunization. Rather is it to promote the optimum health and well-being of all children by the measures indicated in this book. Then it may be found that children will experience these diseases in a positive way without complications, and this disease experience may even confer blessings and new strengths on the child's soul and body.

Social Development

Here we have another matter of concern to parents, another question. "How can I ensure that my child will develop socially? Does he need to attend a crêche once a week for social interaction?"

First of all, let us be quite clear about what is meant by social development. It does *not* mean being the life of the party, being able to make witty and entertaining conversation, able to 'keep up with the Joneses'. It *does* mean an ability to form lasting friendships, to communicate, to have a sense of responsibility for one's own family, the larger community and society as a whole. It is these attributes that concern us when thinking of social development, and we must find ways of preparing the child so that not only will he be a socially acceptable child, but will become a socially responsible adult confidently taking his place within society.

The eminent educators Raymond and Dorothy Moore have much to say about this. "The family and the home are the foundation of our society . . . The small child needs to be with those to whom he best relates. In most cases this will be his parents . . . This warm responsible relationship on a consistent basis is the best foundation a young child can have not only for later schooling, but also for social development."[13] It is interesting that their research has led them to the conviction that "this quality of sociability is more difficult to build into the child who starts school too early".[14]

Again and again all researchers come to the conclusion that what the child needs if he is to develop to his optimum on all levels – and this includes social development – is a warm, happy and fulfilling home life especially during the early years. The Moores consider that the child develops socially more through the example of parents than by attending a crêche or similar group. We have seen that imitation is an early form of learning and if Mother and Dad relate well with each other and with their community the child will copy this.

Most certainly, the toddler or young child does *not* need to be left at a crêche once a week (or more often!) to be socially developed. In fact, that will have the exact opposite effect, for he will be filled with anxiety, and therefore may respond aggressively towards other children and adults, or withdraw into himself.

Equally certainly, Mother needs a day off now and then, and it is a fully legitimate need. We have dealt with this in the previous chapter and suggested a way in which it can be achieved.

Let us sum this up by saying that social development takes place quite naturally in a good-quality home environment, not by the child being thrust into contact with unfamiliar adults and groups of unfamiliar children. An important qualification here is that the home life should be such that the child's basic needs for warmth of heart and play opportunities are met. This brings us to consider play-groups and play-mates.

Play-Groups, Play-Mates and Pre-Schools

Organized play-groups are a comparatively recent phenomenon. In previous generations, larger families were in themselves a play group, and as well as this there was a richer community life. Playing on the village green or on the streets in suburbia provided children with a ready made play-group which arose quite spontaneously.

Today, high-rise flats, isolated families, and constant traffic in most suburban streets have brought about a completely changed situation.

And not only have many children lost the opportunity for spontaneously playing with others, but often mothers feel isolated too. Out of the need caused by this situation, organized play-groups have arisen.

At first these catered for children between the ages of two and three years – that is, for that period of time between toddler and kindergarten age. But as time went on, groups were organized for younger and younger children, until now there are play-groups for the crawling age!

In Melbourne in 1981, the Lady Gowrie Child Centre issued a report entitled *A Must, A Maybe, or A Mistake - Parents and Toddlers Groups*. This was the result of an investigation by Anne Willis Stonehouse, Co-ordinator of Child Care and Parent Programmes.[15] She described one purpose of the report as being "to discourage the wholesale endorsement of groups as the answer to living with one and a half to three year olds."[16]

As there is considerable diversity of opinion regarding the value of play-groups for toddlers, we will look in some detail at this report. Its author has had wide experience in this field and her statements are based on detailed observations and a broad knowledge of her subject. She asks "Do toddlers need groups?" – and answers her question as follows: "The issue of whether toddlers need friends, or other children their own age, is a complex one . . . Researchers who have studied social development in this age group and have observed interaction among young children attest to the interest and enjoyment associated with it, but do not give definitive information about whether or not substantial social experience with other children is necessary or advantageous for under three's to have . . . In fact, this early pressure to share, co-operate, and get along may have the opposite effect. That is, it may impede the child's progress . . . 'she needs other children' does not necessarily mean that she needs *groups* of children . . . Some group experience may be a good thing for some toddlers, but too much will not be helpful . . . It is valuable for young children to learn to enjoy playing alone, to be self-reliant . . . Children who frequently play in groups may be denied that opportunity."[17] In summing up her findings, Anne Willis Stonehouse recognizes that in many cases it is the parents who need opportunity to meet together to discuss the care of their children. This is a different need from that of the toddler.

This report clearly indicates that to assume one's child will be disadvantaged if he does not attend a play-group is a totally wrong assumption. The crux of the matter is – what type of home life does the child have? If he is an only child living in a small upstairs flat and Mother feels lonely and isolated, then to attend a play-group is a tremendous help for both. Mother meets other people, and the child has a change of scene. But if there is garden space for playing, creative parents, and Mother has a number of outside interests, then a toddler is in no way disadvantaged by not attending a play-group. In fact, it is desirable that from an early age he has opportunity to initiate play out of his own resources, and to experience solitude (very different from loneliness).

Toddlers do not need group experiences. Mothers very often do.

Yet, a child of this age will often respond in a friendly way to another child, and such contact is frequently achieved during visits to friends. Later on, from about two years of age onwards, playmates become desirable. Here, the child next door, one in the neighbourhood, or a visiting relative or friend fulfils this need. A neighbourhood group which arises spontaneously is the ideal play-group for this age. "May I go and play with Mary, please Mummy?" or, "We'll ask John over to play this afternoon" means playing in a familiar setting with a familiar child. This is the age of 'along-side' play mentioned in the previous chapter. A good-quality home setting meets all its needs.

However, if parents do decide on a play-group for their toddler or two year old, and this can certainly be beneficial for an only child with no playmates, it is desirable to attend one where there is only a small number of children – say three, or at the very most four. "In general, the smaller the group the better" says Anne Willis Stonehouse.[18] Structured programes for children of this age (all sitting at tables or on a mat together for a common activity) are totally inappropriate; and to direct a toddler to share toys or expect him to communicate with other children is also inappropriate and doomed to failure.

Older children of three to four years and upwards are ready for group play. Today this usually means attendance at a kindergarten or pre-school. This has the added advantage of giving Mother some time off. But even at this age, a child in a large family where siblings become playmates, will find all his needs within an adequate home life.[19] This also applies to the children of families who live in isolated country areas.

Parents whose nearest neighbour is miles away need not feel that their children will grow into unsociable adults or will be at any disadvantage at all. In fact a full life in the country, sharing farm activities, is the best possible environment for children. Like a crèche, play-groups and pre-school experience have nothing to do with social development.

However, for a city child within a small family, attendance at a kindergarten where the programme is based on a knowledge of the child's soul and spiritual needs can give much. It also gives opportunity for parents to meet each other and share experiences amongst themselves and with the kindergarten teacher. This can often be of great value.

Pre-school programmes designed to 'educate' the child in a 'realistic' way are to be avoided. They work with the child's thinking instead of his will. The T.V. programme Sesame Street is one example of this.

There are diverse points of view about pre-school and primary school education. It may, therefore be helpful to parents to look at a method which stands for an approach almost the opposite to that which we have been discussing. This is the Montessori method. It is one of many different methods of education, and its principles apply also to the pre-school years. We choose to consider it because it is well known and well established in a number of countries. We will state some of the basic principles as set out by its founder. This is not said by way of criticism, but to help parents make an objective appraisal.

The Montessori method is concerned primarily with "the furthering of (children's) intellectual growth";[20] it denies the significance of play, fantasy and imagination. Maria Montessori describes play as a 'trivial occupation', and further comments, "I realized that in the life of a child play is perhaps something of little importance which he undertakes for lack of something better to do."[21]

Speaking of "childish traits and deviations" which disappear in children attending such a school, Maria Montessori lists "so-called 'creative imagination', delight in stories, attachment to individuals, play . . . and so forth . . . Also traits such as imitation (and) curiosity. . . " She says "A child's imagination (which) can give symbolic meaning to any object whatever, creates fantastic mirages within his mind . . . a chair becomes a throne, a stone an airplane. Children are given toys with which they can play, but which create illusions and afford no real and productive contact with reality . . . they cannot provide any real mental concentration but only illusions . . . Teachers discover that highly imaginative children are not the best in their studies as might be expected. Instead, they achieve little or nothing at all." She considers that "this weakening of a child's intellectual powers occurs when his mind takes flight into a world of illusion."[22]

Such are some of the principles and bases of this particular method of education as set out by its founder.

Guiding Behaviour - the Establishment of Good Habits

The establishment of good habits belongs to the second seven years. But in the early years, parents can prepare by setting examples and introducing the child to certain desirable patterns of behaviour. It is an introductory phase; the actual formation of the habit comes later.

What constitutes good behaviour and good habits and differentiates them from bad behaviour and bad habits will vary from family to family and from generation to generation. It is a matter of parents' own values and judgements. What is of importance to some parents, for example table manners, may be regarded as conventional or superficial by others. However, parents should be aware that whatever their standards and values *the child needs guidance in these areas from the earliest years*. Lack of guidance leads inevitably to 'the terrible two's'.

We have seen that at first, children learn by imitation. Therefore the best way of influencing behaviour is to practise the desired habit oneself. This may entail saying 'please' and 'thank you'; it may involve putting one's own things away tidily; washing one's hands before meals, or, as above, setting an example in table manners. To quietly but firmly insist on a certain standard of behaviour does not mean bullying the child. It means having his future well-being at heart, and providing a framework of standards within which he will have adequate freedom and scope for his adventurous spirit. Mother decides when it is bath time or bed time, and if there are protests , simply picks up her vigorous protestor and calmly and cheerfully carries him to bath or bedroom. A child will soon learn that Mother and Dad mean what they say! Therefore it is important for parents to act responsibly, consistently and fairly towards the child. It must be remembered that the child looks to his parents for guidance, and what Mother and Dad say and do, is for him right and proper.

Here we must differentiate between authority and

authoritarianism. The latter wields the big stick, often shouts and is in every way deplorable. But the true authority which a child seeks is always quietly spoken, it is very firm and serious, expects to be obeyed, and is recognized as such by the child. Here there is no place for shouting, for the firmness and seriousness of the parental direction cannot be mistaken. Children of parents who firmly insist on obedience are much happier and more secure than those whose parents oscillate, or worse still, are ruled by the child.[23]

A common error is to expect a young child to be capable of making a choice. "Would you like toast or porridge for breakfast?" is an exercise in futility before there is a thinking capacity able to make judgements. "Are you ready for your bath yet?" or "Would you like to have your bath now?" is equally futile and places an unrealistic demand on the child's capacity for rational response.

Piaget, in relation to an eight year old, considered that "the child's process of reasoning is certainly very confused;" and found that "young children (6 to 10 year olds) seldom express causal relations."[24]

How much better for the child when Mother, in a cheerful and authoritative voice says, "Bathtime now! come and get undressed." and at meal times simply places the food in front of the child. This method, *practised from the very beginning,* gives the child the guidance his soul seeks, and provides a reasonable family framework for daily activities. It also inculcates a healthy respect for parents which is an essential ingredient in any successful child/parent relationship. In later life, this childhood respect is often expressed as affection and admiration.

It is a strong will force, not a pre-meditated plan which drives a toddler or young child into doing something which he knows is forbidden territory – pulling up Mother's indoor plants, experimenting on the window pane with Dad's hammer. Let us recall that children 'know' before they understand; he has been admonished for this exciting experiment and knows it is out of bounds. Yet, again and again he attempts it, keeping an eye on Mother as he edges nearer the desired oject. He is helpless to control the power of his will force and is ruled by it.

To cope with this situation, it is good if parents use a certain firm and very serious tone of voice, a special word and a hand and facial gesture to denote forbidden territory. One needs to go near the child, make eye contact, and speak quietly with the utmost seriousness.

Shouting across the room will achieve nothing of lasting value; and this applies also to making a joke of the situation. The child needs to be bodily removed to another area of the room, and given something equally enticing to do. Ultimately he will come to recognise that this is the out-of-bounds signal, and after countless repetitions, and a gradual maturation of his brain, he will be less a victim of instinctual will drives. We have seen that repetition is an early method of learning. Parents must expect to give the same direction day after day, week after week, and probably year after year. Of course it is commonsense during this period to remove from sight tempting and dangerous objects.

It must be added that some children have what can be called a mischievous quality. They are usually small-headed children with a rapidly closing fontanelle, bright eyed, alert and 'into everything'. The reader is reminded of what was said about this type of child in Chapter Ten (section on vegetables) and Appendix K.

These practices need to be introduced right from the beginning. It is useless and only causes endless pain to parents and child if patterns of desired behaviour are imposed at three or four years of age when previously there has been no such guidance. The child then rebels with tears and tantrums, and parents feel frustrated, upset and sometimes angry.

Until puberty, the child in his inner being is fundamentally innocent. Like Adam in the Garden of Eden, he has not yet gone through the 'Fall'. He longs to be 'good', and to be loved by his parents. This is the deepest yearning of his heart. Deviant behaviour often arises because the child is bombarded by the products of our technical age, his senses and whole being assaulted by 20th Century civilization and those modern theories on child care which deny his essential spirituality.

It is these things, coupled with a lack of firm guidance which very largely cause the 'problems' of which we hear so much. It makes no sense asking the child to 'promise to be good', when all his experiences of life continously erode the innocence of his soul.

It is one of the tasks of this book to attempt to bring these matters to the attention of parents and others; to offer a point of view which has the possibility of preventing behavioural problems arising, and of bringing a healing influence to children already aggressive or withdrawn. It is worthwhile repeating in this context, that artistic activities are the great healers.

The child who has grown up always knowing kindly, firm authority, and who has quite naturally developed desirable patterns of behaviour will be a popular child and a self-disciplined and authoritative adult.

Challenges

Life is full of challenges. Through facing them we grow in strength. The suffering they frequently cause gives opportunity for inner growth. Thus it is for us adults. How is it for the child?

Children also need challenges to equip them for facing those of later life. We must understand the sequence in which these should occur.

During the first seven years challenges should be *only in the will*, not in the emotions or thinking. They should be such that the child can resolve them through his 'doing'. Play gives opportunity for this. On the emotional level it is ideal that Mother and Dad be living 'happily ever after', and the child encompassed by an atmosphere of soul warmth. Intense emotional experiences are inappropriate for the young child. We have described the thinking of this stage as having a picture-doing character. This has not the rationality to deal with challenges out of its own forces. It is in the will alone that the young child is able successfully to face challenge. Here it is beneficial.

During the second seven year period children are able to face challenges in their feeling. A child of nine will deeply grieve the death of a beloved dog, and with support will be able to work through this. A child of three may be affected for a short time, but will soon recover especially if the family acquires a new puppy. The younger child's sadness is much more superficial than that of his older sibling. During this time challenges in the will can take the form of jobs and responsibilities in the home within the child's capabilities. Making one's own bed, tidying one's room before going to school, or if living in the country, feeding the fowls and collecting the eggs. These are examples of home duties which meet the will's need for a more mature challenge, and prepare the child for future responsibilities.

It is during the third seven years that challenges occur in the thinking. Questions arise such as – "What is life all about? Has it any meaning? Why am I here? – Who am I?" and "Is there any purpose in the scheme of things?" These are real challenges in the thinking sphere. They confront the teenager with great intensity; he is challenged, through his thinking, to find satisfactory solutions. At puberty, emotional challenges become greatly intensified; and high school studies and examinations challenge both thinking and will.

Thus is the sequence of challenge for the child.

Three Human Skills

During the first seven years, the child acquires three skills not attained by any other creature. They are walking upright, articulate speech, and independent thinking. The first two of these are learned. Thinking, on the other hand, "fills the being of the child from the beginning. It is in existence and at work, but has no possibility as yet to show itself. It dwells in the distant depths of the child's existence."[25]

We have already indicated the great significance of the human upright posture, and have seen that the child strives to achieve this right from the earliest weeks. It has also been noted that the kitten and foal are ever satisfied with the horizontal, and even the great apes do not achieve a true uprightness. (See Chapter Seven.) It is man alone who truly points his head to the heavens. Most children achieve this between approximately ten to fifteen months of age.

Speech develops through gurgling and cooing to babbling, then single syllable words to short sentences. If we listen carefully to the first stage, that of gurgling and cooing, we will hear that it is comprised of vowel sounds. Through these the baby expresses his feelings. As adults we also use vowels for this purpose – 'ah', 'ee', 'oh', 'oo'. Later on, at about six or seven months, the child begins to experiment with consonants. Usually 'M', 'D' and 'B' emerge first, and develop into 'Mama', 'Dada' and 'Bub-Bub'. We need consonants for naming things, and now the baby slowly learns to name all things and creatures.

We have already seen that the child is a microcosm of vast macrocosmic processes; in his development he mirrors the long journey of mankind. This also applies to the development of his speech. This process is portrayed in biblical story. In the book of Genesis, Chapter Two we read, "And out of the ground the Lord God formed every beast of the field, and every fowl of the air; and brought them unto Adam to see what he would call them; and whatsoever Adam called every living creature, that was the name thereof. And Adam gave names to all cattle, and the fowl of the air, and to every beast of the field . . . "

This portrays a very early stage of man's speech development. Prior to this, he only made sounds which expressed his feelings. The ability to name things came later as the first beginnings of memory appeared.[26]

This can be clearly seen in the child; for at about six months of age the baby, like Adam, begins to find names for things. He has reached Chapter Two of Genesis.

As remembering and speech develop from tender bud to blossom, so does the gift of thinking slowly emerge. This happens at about three years of age. "In the child's third year it is really as if the sun of thinking were to appear above the horizon and brightly illuminate the relations that have been formed between all his experiences."[27] Slowly, slowly thinking will grow until it becomes independent of action and is able to be truly reflective.

It may be objected that the animals also think, and this of course is true. Anyone who has worked with a cattle or sheep dog will know this. But the thinking of the animal is tied to the action, to the present moment. The dog has to be actually engaged in mustering the cattle to be thinking about them. He is unable to sit in his kennel afterwards and reflect upon the day's work and the habits of cattle. He acts in the now, out of thought-filled instinct. But "in man, thoughts attain an independent existence, transcending the immediate experience."[28]

To observe the child's development in this light and to reflect upon it, gives further insight into the uniqueness of man, and the many marvels contained within the child.

Soul Virtues, Graces and Prayers

We will finish this chapter by looking briefly at what Rudolf Steiner calls "basic soul virtues".[29] He describes the three most fundamental of these as gratitude, love and duty. These awaken in the child over the three seven year rhythms and need to be understood and fostered. Their active cultivation at the appropriate times offers a practical means of helping to overcome many of today's social problems.

"Gratitude is the basic virtue in the child's soul between birth and the change of teeth."[30] To foster this does not imply that the child should be constantly told he must be grateful for this or that. Rather it is an attitude of soul in the parents, portrayed in speech and gesture that the child will imitate. It can be expressed in a number of ways – a simple grace before meals thanking the earth and sun for giving and ripening the food; or a short prayer at bed-time looking with wonder and reverence to the heavens. The following grace for young children was given by Rudolf Steiner. It can be said by the parents or the whole family when seated at the table.

> Earth that gave us all this food
> Sun that made it ripe and good
> Dear Sun, dear Earth
> We pray that ye
> Never shall forgotten be.

Everybody then holds hands and says together "blessings on the meal". It is a simple ceremony and can give a great deal to a child.

As the children grow older and become familiar with the idea of a bounteous God – perhaps through Old Testament stories – the grace can incorporate this.

> Great Spirit of God who made all things
> From whose hands came all that's good
> Who fashioned birds and honey-bees
> And made the flowers and fruit and trees
> We give you thanks for all these things
> And ask your blessing on our food.

To say a short prayer at bedtime also gives a great deal. The child carries it into his sleep in the form of pictures which arise in his soul. This is real soul nourishment and can be a tremendous help to a wakeful restless child. The prayer is best said by candlelight after the bedtime story, in an atmosphere of calm and reverence. The prayer should not be taught to the child; if parents say it each night, the child will soon learn it and then all can say it together.

> As I go to sleep each night
> An angel watches o'er me
> And fills my soul with flooding light
> And guides me to the stars so bright
> And blesses me each morning.

This is suitable for the very young. And for the older child whose soul can accommodate more than one picture –

Peeping out of heaven's height
Like glowing candles burning bright
The stars look down from heaven.
And guarding angels there I see
Making music joyously
Always watching over me
And sending us their blessing.

There are other soul virtues which can be prepared in the early years. A caring attitude is one of these. Here again, parental example is the main teacher, not continual admonishment. The child can be encouraged to care for birds by helping Mother fill the bird-bath; he can help her prepare a casserole for a sick neighbour, share the caring for an injured animal. A child will absorb such attitudes into himself, making them part of his own soul.

Fostering attitudes of caring, reverence and gratitude – saying grace and a simple prayer – some people may consider this too idealistic for the late 20th Century, too old-fashioned. Yet it is only by the practice of such soul virtues that distress and strife at all levels can be mitigated and eventually overcome. Perhaps 'peace on earth' is a long way off. On the other hand it could be surprisingly near if all children were given a chance by parental example and guidance to so enrich their souls.

Chapter Fifteen
The Constitution of the Soul

Again we must turn to the human soul, and probe within ourself. Our gaze will range over ordinary mundane experiences of everyday life to the far reaches of our most illuminated thoughts and moral impulses – such is the prodigious range of the soul's orbit. It reaches to far-flung fields encompassing both earth and heaven.

We can speak about the 'principles' or 'members' of the soul; or adopt Dr Karl König's terminology of 'geography' of the soul with its various 'landscapes';[1] or again, liken it to our body, and describe it in terms of its 'constitution'. For, just as the body is constituted with various members – limb system, excretory organs, reproductive system, etc. – so is the soul. In caring for a child, it is of the greatest importance to understand these soul members, for only then can decisions really be made relating to education, suitable sensory experiences, whether or not to encourage fantasy play and so on. *Knowledge of the soul is basic for modern parenting.*

We will begin with our everyday experiences.

We are eating an orange. We experience a sensation of sweetness and feel pleasure.

We are shopping and see a blue coat. We feel the softness or roughness of its texture. We experience a desire to buy it, and our will is stirred to try it on.

We are in the garden looking at a red rose. We smell and touch it, and experience sensations of redness and smoothness. We feel disappointed because it has no perfume. A blackbird begins to sing. We listen, our disappointment vanishes and we begin to feel a joy in the bird-song.

In these three situations we *perceive* the outside world through our sense organs, and sensations and various experiences arise *within* us. It is a materialistic fallacy to argue that sensations and emotions have their origin in the nervous system.[2] Nerve cells are made from material substance, as are the grains of the sea sand. Neither has a capacity for inner experiencing. Sensations and emotions arise within the soul which uses the nerve-sense organization as its perceiving instrument. Here we have the first soul member. Rudolf Steiner calls it the 'Sentient soul'[3] because it gives the experience of sensations, and is closely connected with the sense organs. We will refer to it as the 'Experiencing Principle', for it gives us the ability to experience the world which we perceive.

As we continue to explore our inner life, we soon recognise that not only do we experience the world, but we also are able to gather information about it, and work out how to satisfy the desires which arise within us. We have a rational analysing principle in the mind. We are able to put things into categories, take out statistics, make plans and form logical conclusions. This is the intellect or rational mind. We will call it the 'Intellectual Principle' of the soul. It uses the brain for its thinking instrument, just as the pianist uses the piano for his playing instrument. But the intellect is not the *product* of the brain, any more than the pianist is the product of the piano. The body is the foundation of the soul life, not its progenitor.[4]

But we must not stop here! There is a further soul principle, one which opens its portals and gives the soul access to the light and love of the spirit. The German word used by Steiner to describe this is *Bewusstseinsseele*.[5] We will call it the soul's 'Higher Principle'.

These soul principles can be thought of as weaving, light-filled colours reaching out into different fields of life; or, as different 'areas' of our inner life, and in the latter picture, Karl König's representation of 'landscapes' is helpful. The Experiencing Principle could be likened to the lowlands. Into this flows everything which we perceive – like rivers and streams flowing down to the plains. Our intellect could be likened to the hills and valleys, for with our rational mind we can reach up to the heights or plunge down to the depths of immorality and crime. Then there is the alpine region, the lofty peaks of the soul through which we grasp the truth of all things and come to know the love of the Divine.

Thus is the soul constituted. We must now explore ways of incorporating this knowledge into our upbringing of the child. Only if we can do that, will the soul develop into a fount of warmth and radiant colour, streaming out into the world, and at the same time gathering treasures of experience and knowledge, serving the needs of the human spirit throughout the length of life.

Let us now address our task . . .

It has been stated above that the sense organs serve the soul's Experiencing Principle just as the brain serves its Intellectual Principle. It goes without saying that a well-developed intellectual capacity depends upon a healthy and well-developed brain. If the brain is damaged, the child (or adult) becomes either partially or totally intellectually retarded according to the degree of damage.

So it is with the Experiencing Principle. An adult capacity to experience life in its fullness depends upon healthy and well-developed sense organs. If the sense organs are damaged (especially during the first seven years), there will be a partial or total incapacity for inner experiencing according to the degree of damage.

A marked difference between the former and the latter of these two forms of retardation is that brain damage and intellectual retardation manifest almost immediately, whereas sensory damage and an incapacity to experience life is more subtle, and manifests much more gradually. Its eventual expression is found in a barrenness of soul, an inner hollow emptiness which becomes visible in the drug scene and high suicide rate amongst young adults.[6]

While no responsible parent would expose his or her child to brain damage – for instance, by leaving a six months' old infant alone on a table, or at the top of a flight of stairs – many people unthinkingly expose their children to sensory damage. Both of these forms of retardation, either partial or total, are equally detrimental to a successful life.

In Chapter Eleven we considered helpful and harmful sense impressions. Here, in preparing the child's soul, we see a further impelling reason for parents to take to heart what was said there. This particularly applies to television viewing. We must now add to its many destructive effects, damage to the soul. There is a straight and inevitable path leading from the child who is constantly exposed to sensory damage, to the adult who has the barrenness of soul mentioned above. In all walks of life today we see its devastating effects.

The often expressed point of view which says that children "have got to get used to it; they've got to learn to handle it", shows a complete lack of understanding of the human soul and the need for preparation of its functions and principles throughout childhood. It is a point of view arising from a tragic misconception and its full effect on humanity is yet to be seen.

It was the Greek philosophers such as Aristotle, Socrates and Plato who prepared the intellect for mankind. It is this wonderful gift which we now use every day and simply take for granted. We constantly call upon it to work things out, solve problems, amass information, analyse situations, fulfil desires, form abstractions, theorize, philosophize, and, in fact, conduct our daily life. What a wonderful thinking tool it is! It forms the very foundation of present day science and technology, and provides the myriad goods and conveniences which we constantly use. We cannot imagine life without it!

Yet, in spite of the many blessings it bestows, the intellect has two tremendous limitations. They can be stated as follows –

Firstly, *the intellect per se is amoral*. It can produce a plan of unselfish service for the benefit of others, or work out the elaborate details of a dishonest scheme or major crime, both with equal efficiency. It makes no difference whether the scheme be 'good' or 'bad'. The intellect can analyse and plan details of either with equal competence. The master mind of the criminal is nothing more or less than a highly developed intellect acting solely out of itself. Here there is no warmth of soul, no illumination or goodness. To ensure that rational thinking will be used in a moral way, requires something more than the intellect's own intrinsic powers.

Secondly *the intellect, out of itself, cannot arrive at the higher absolute truths*. To illustrate this, let us look with our rational mind only, at one of the most profound statements ever made – "In the beginning was the Word." A rational argument would go something like this . . . "If there were a word, it must have been composed of letters, and therefore the letters must have come before the word. If there were letters, there must have been somebody already there to design and write them. Therefore," says the rational mind,"'In the beginning was the word' can only be described as nonsense; it cannot be rationally substantiated." That is the only honest conclusion that can be arrived at *in this way*. To grasp the truth of these profound words requires the use of the soul's Higher Principle. Their meaning is beyond the reach of the intellect's own power.

These two limitations of the intellect need to be recognized if foundations are to be laid to ensure a future capacity for moral action and a grasp of truth. To assume that a well-developed intellect is the highest human attribute is to invite untold dangers and errors, frequently damaging to the child's future.

We now come to consider the soul's Higher Principle, the *Bewusstseinsseele*. (Consciousness Soul.) The German infinitive *zu wissen* means to know; and the past tense *gewusst* means known. If I wished to say "I have known that, I would use *Ich habe das gewusst.*

The *Bewusstseinsseele* is the 'knowing soul', the soul principle through which we become conscious or aware of something. This knowing is not arrived at by an analytical process or an amassing of detailed information; rather is it a *seeing*, a pictorial grasping of the whole.

We turn again to the idiom of language to gain insight. We have been grappling inwardly with a problem, turning it over in our mind, brooding upon it. Then, either suddenly in a flash, or gradually over a period of several days, we come to *see* the solution; we *know* what it's all about; we 'get the *picture*', and we 'see the *light*'. As the light of truth floods into our soul, the mind takes it up, incorporates it into itself, and forms it into concepts. It is highly beneficial to attempt to observe this process in oneself. If, after some practice, this is achieved, it will be seen that at the moment of 'getting the picture' and 'seeing the light', *the intellect is not engaged*. Only the Higher Principle of the soul is active. It beholds the truth as a totality.

To recognize this is of immense importance. Let us emphasize it! *Man has a faculty which transcends the limitations of the intellect.*

When man has learned to use this Higher Principle, he is able to reach out through his seeing-knowing-thinking, and come into contact with that which is of an eternal nature. He transcends both the intellect and the soul's Experiencing Principle. Rudolf Steiner describes it thus . . .

"By causing the self-existent true and good to come to life in his inner being, man raises himself above the mere sentient soul. The eternal spirit shines into it. In so far as the soul lives in this light, it is a participant of the eternal. It unites therewith its own existence. What the soul carries in it of the true and the good is immortal in it."[7]

It is this activity which fructifies the whole soul, bringing light to the intellect and a capacity to work with love. This illuminated and goodness-filled soul is portrayed in the fairy stories as the beautiful Princess. When the Prince, the higher self (or Ego) finds and marries this pure soul, they live happily ever after. (See Chapter Thirteen.)

Furthermore, the activity of the Higher Principle not only illuminates the intellect, but brings about its actual expansion and enlargement. Rudolf Steiner describes it clearly:

" . . . the intellectual soul (i.e. the intellect) grows the larger the more it receives into itself of the true and the good. For this true and good cause the expansion of the intellectual soul."[8]

These words should be writ large over every educational institution today:

It is the light of the spirit which causes the expansion of the intellect.

When this happens, the intellect, immersing itself in the eternal light of truth and warmth of goodness, expands and reaches its full stature. It opens like a flower and reaches up to the light and warmth of the great sun.

It is not a bigger and better I.Q. which brings illumination and goodness to the human mind. These qualities are of the spirit. They stream into the soul the more man has learned to activate his will, develop his feelings, and use his imaginative thinking. For when using the Higher Principle, the soul engages its three functions of will, feeling and thinking. It is a total involvement.

The possession of a higher soul principle is one of the many things which raises man above the beasts. Nature, with her prodigal fecundity, has produced many marvels; and while her wisdom constantly amazes us, she is unable to reach to the sublime heights. The thinking dog, the building beaver, the purring cat are creatures inexorably limited by their very 'dogness', 'beaverness' and 'catness'. They are tied to instinct and Nature's wisdom. Here there is no freedom.

Man transcends Nature. He is the only creature who, through his soul, is able to reach out to his creator, to be in contact with the source of his origin, and with humility and gratitude seek in freedom to serve the Divine.

Finally in this discussion we must ask, "How can the capacities of this Higher Principle be prepared during childhood?" The question involves both home caring and education.

The child must be prepared for a 'seeing' capacity. This means, above all, giving opportunity for fantasy play, and telling the fairy stories. Here the child sees something which is not physically present. His fantasy and pictorial imagination take wing. It is this which must be encouraged and given full rein in the early years.

There is 'dressing up' in Mother's and Dad's cast-off garments; being a nurse, a shop-keeper, travelling to the furthest star, going off to fairyland on a magic carpet – entering into a world of make-believe which the child pictures inwardly. It is this which can ripen into the seeing soul. Fantasy, like fairy tales, prepares a pictorial knowing. Today, children desperately need it.

Later come myths and legends to fire the child's imagination and feeling. These find a fruitful basis in the earlier fairy tales and fantasy life.

Such knowledge of the soul's constitution as we have been

discussing, has far-reaching implications for the home care and education of children. It means that parents and educators must be deeply concerned with the whole body and the whole soul. Sense impressions, fantasy play, opportunities for being active in limbs, heart and head *at the right time*, all these things take on new and wide-flung dimensions affecting each individual and thus the whole of humanity.

It is an immense and urgent responsibility hardly yet recognized. Many parents today just begin to sense it as they seek 'to do the right thing'. Their children are the hope of tomorrow.

Chapter Sixteen
The Development of Thinking

Only now, with the soul's full range of possibilities in view, and with knowledge of the unfolding rhythm of its functions, are we in a position to consider the development of thinking throughout childhood.

It was Rudolf Steiner who said that man "can find his path to knowledge only when thinking is his starting point."[1] The crucial question here is, what type of thinking does he mean? Is he speaking of deductive logic, abstract thinking, inspired thinking . . . or what?

He further comments that "man can only come to a true understanding of himself when he grasps clearly the significance of thinking within his being."[2]

He first describes a type of thinking which serves to satisfy our daily needs. It is a thinking with which we are very familiar. Steiner describes it as thinking "in the first place", and calls it the product of the 'Intellectual Soul'.[3] It serves our everyday life, and has produced our technological society. But it is not the "thinking (which) is the highest of the faculties possessed by man in the world of the senses".[4] That is something quite different.

Rudolf Steiner describes thoughts which contain within them a *picture* of truth as carrying a living force. " . . . thought is a living force", and further, "This force will be active in him (man); it will awaken slumbering capacities."[5]

In view of this, it behoves us to come to some understanding of the development of the child's thinking, so that seeds can be planted which in later years will blossom into this active thought force. It is the force needed to use the Higher Principle of the soul, that part of our being through which we gain knowledge, and illuminate and warm the intellect as already described.

Piaget considers that "from birth to about two years, the infant is unable to think; he can only perform overt actions."[6] It is during this period that the rate of growth of the brain is greatest. After about two years, the growth rate markedly drops. (See Appendix L.) As explained previously, it is during these early years that the brain should be left as undisturbd as possible if it is to be built up to reach its full potential.

An observation of the child of about three or four years clearly reveals that his thinking is connected with what is going on in his immediate environment. If he is playing in the sandpit, he is thinking of sandcastles. His speech reveals this. "Now I'm making a bigger one." "I'm going to build a bridge near my castle." And, in the dolls' corner – "I'm the mummy and you're the daddy." "No, I'm the postman bringing the letters." As stated in Chapter Twelve, it is a picture-doing-thinking; and as such, it fulfils the child's needs, for, as we have seen, he is awake in his limb system, not in his head system.

These observations are in line with some of Piaget's basic ideas. After many observations he came to the conclusion that "the thought of younger children was *qualitatively different* from that of older ones."[7] And, "The real problem of intelligence . . . was to discover the different methods of thinking used by children of various ages . . . (Piaget's) study of infancy convinced him that thought derived from the child's action, and not from his language."[8] His experiences of young children led him "to place emphasis on the role of the child's activity in the formation of thought . . . Knowledge of reality must be discovered and constructed by the activity of the child. He is able to act only on things which he can perceive directly."[9]

Here we have confirmation from an authority in this field that the child's thinking is indeed connected with his activity within the immediate environment; and in this way he learns. It is a thinking full of promise for the future; for the creative thinking of the adult is the matured will-penetrated picture thinking of the child. This early type of thinking will only fulfil its promise if the child is allowed to practise and perfect it. Early education techniques inhibit its development. This includes teaching babies to read, and T.V. programmes such as Sesame Street.

In the second seven years, all that was developed earlier is carried over and becomes fructified with feeling as the child lives more and more within his rhythmic system. The simple picture thinking expands into wider imaginations, and thinking and feeling learn to work together. This could be called an imaginative-feeling-thinking. It is certainly not deductive or abstract. Again, to call on Piaget . . . He is speaking of six to seven year olds. "Children do not attempt to explain events to one another . . . (they) do not try to give proof or logical justification . . . " He considers that children of this age are unable "to state causal relations." He found that at seven years "the child first solves problems on the plane of action", and it is not until about eleven years of age that he is able to "express his solutions on the plane of verbal thought."[10]

We have seen above that thoughts which contain within them a *picture* of the truth, carry a living force. It is this force which works on the child's thinking, inspiring it, firing it with imagination, preparing it to later serve the soul's Higher Principle. This means that parents and teacher must be able to present the truth of things in vivid pictures.

We are here in the realm of fairy tales, myths and legends, for as we have seen, these contain, concealed within them, profound truths which speak to the child. When they are brought to life by an imaginative parent or school teacher, and told in such a way that pictures arise in the child's mind, then a first building block is laid for later pictorial thinking.

Once the child is able to read, he can be given books of myths and legends. The heroic epics of the Greeks, the sea-faring sagas of the great Viking heroes, the Sumerian legend of Gilgamesh, Germanic fairy tales, and English legends of St George and the knights of the Round Table, all of these are indispensable if a child is to have the opportunity to develop his thinking to its fullest capacity.

It is interesting and encouraging that in a lecture given in Melbourne on May 22, 1985, Professor Kieren Egan of the Simon Fraser University, Canada spoke of various stages of educational development, one of which is the 'mythic'.[11]

We now come to the third seven years and the birth and development of the intellect. Piaget puts it thus " . . . the final period of intellectual development, is that . . . which begins at about age 12, and is consolidated during adolescence."[12] He considers that this can only be reached if the child has already established a basis for it. "Manipulation of things (that is, 'doing') is a prerequisite for higher verbal understanding. The young child cannot jump to the higher levels before establishing a basis in concrete manipulation."[13]

It is at this stage that all that has gone before, all that has been carried forward, begins to mature and becomes fertilized by logical concepts. It is now understood in a rational way. Also, forces of will and this clear thinking begin to work together, so direction and a sense of purpose emerge. Feelings come to bear upon this, emotions stir and the teenager is filled with enthusiasm as he looks to the future. With his newly-formed sense of direction he is able to plan ahead, he knows where he's going, he has a purpose in life. Now a new and exciting world opens up as the thinking pursues higher learning. It is an age of discovery, an age of passionate feelings and ideas.

This is what the adolescent years have to offer if that which has gone before has been wisely guided by parents and teachers. But all too frequently today we see a very different picture. Often the brain has been 'programmed' into one-way intellectualism in the early years, and there is no room for a more expansive thinking to arise. Then there emerges a sterile one-way mentality within which thought is confined. It may be clever, but there is a lack of warmth and inner mobility. Or again, the feeling life may have been neglected and so failed to mature. In this case, during the teenage years, and indeed, throughout life, there can be observed a separation between feeling and thinking. If the will is strong and the temperament uncontrolled this can be a tremendous danger. We see its manifestation in vandalism and other forms of violence. In these, there is no compassion, no reverence for life, no joy – only an undisciplined will, often directed by a cold and calculating thinking.

And what comes next? We have spoken of a Higher Principle of the soul, one which gives knowledge and illumination. We described it as a seeing-knowing-thinking, one which is fired by will and warmed by feeling. It is this which Steiner referred to when he described thinking as "the highest of the faculties possessed by man in the world of the senses."

As Piaget pointed out, the further step in the thinking of the adolescent can only be reached if a basis has been established earlier. This is exactly what applies to this higher form of thinking. It needs a basis in all that has been developed throughout the childhood years; it cannot grow out of nothing.

This is a thinking which transcends the mind's previous achievements, but at the same time lifts them to a higher level. It is a faculty which can only be developed gradually throughout the adult years. If achieved, it can lead to wisdom.

Chapter Seventeen
The Years Ahead

The child speaks:

It has been an exciting journey. First, leaving the realm of abundant light and plunging down into the darkness of a confined space, an infinitesimal cell; a dimming of consciousness, a placing oneself into the very body of another, there to await nine long months the development of my own body.

Then the cataclysm! the pushing and contractions, the pressure on the head, the slipping downwards, downwards, the narrow tunnel, and then at last, what is this? – air and solidity. All is warmth and light, body to body, and loving hands welcoming, caressing. For an instant there is recognition. A process of redemption and fulfilment has begun.

Thank you for this body. It is a generous gift. As yet it is helpless, but the brain is growing fast and consciousness increasing. Skills are developing. The body is being brought under control, and is now able to be used with some efficiency. Slowly, slowly the journey continues through toddling stage and kindergarten years. And now, seven full years and nine months later, what is this? – a totally new body built up according to guidelines brought from the pristine realm of spirit. With a final triumphant gesture the last remnants of the old body – the teeth – are cast out.

The future lies ahead, school days beckon, the unknown has to be faced. I experience a quiet confidence, a sense of well-beingness, for the first seven years have given much; there are strengths in soul and body. I am grateful.

Thus speaks the child as he stands in the doorway of the future. A great deal has depended on his preparation, and a great deal more will depend upon his future.

Now the ego faces new tasks. Throughout the first seven years the body of life forces has undergone what could be called its own embryonic development. It is now ready for birth. Whether it will be perfect or malformed depends almost entirely on the quality of nurture the child has received during its period of gestation – the first seven years of life. This subtle body can also be called 'the health body'.[1] It is the bearer of the immune system.

During the second seven years, the ego penetrates these vital health forces, working with them according to its own purpose. The process of incarnation moves from material to life; and, as we have seen, growth forces now work strongly on the rhythmic system of heart and lungs. This is the time for music and art in all its forms; and for the rhythmic games mentioned previously.

Rudolf Steiner has described this life body as being "the vehicle of memory, of lasting habits, of temperament and inclinations and enduring desires."[2] Now these features must become the concern of parents. It will be remembered that the child looks to the parents for authoritative guidance. Steiner puts it thus: "We must take every care to develop these features; we must influence a child's habits, his memory, everything which will give his character a firm foundation. The child will grow up like a Will-o'-the-wisp if care is not taken to imbue his character with certain lasting habits, so that with their aid he will stand firm against the storms of life. This, too, is the time for exercising his memory; memorising is more difficult after this age. It is at this time also that a feeling for art awakens, particularly for the art of music. If any musical talent exists, this is when we should do all we can to encourage it. Care must be taken to see that the child learns as much as possible through stories and analogies. We must store his memory with them . . . We must bring before him examples taken from the lives of the great men of history . . . We can hardly place too many such (word) pictures or examples before the child."[3]

In this way does the child's life body increase in vitality and good health, building up the immune system to be a bulwark against diseases in later life.

At puberty, a similar process takes place as strong soul forces undergo 'birth', and again, the ego has a task here. Now the child enters the age of independence, the age of passion, of rational thinking, and of co-ordination as the soul powers of will, feeling and thinking learn to work together. It is a marvellous age, full of new liberating possibilities. How tragic that it is often so violent or so barren.

Thus the child goes through the teenage years and becomes an adult. Now a totally new situation develops. During the preceding twenty-one years everything was given; the three bodies were born and grew. The 'I' was not responsible for this; their birth took place naturally. The ego's task was to fashion them, to prepare its own dwelling place.

But from this point onwards things will be different, for now the 'I' must take charge. Gradually, over the next span of twenty-one years, the ego must learn to use and further develop all that the parents have so painstakingly laid in the soul; the foundation-stones must be built upon. This work I must undertake myself. Whether the beginning has been good or bad, helpful or harmful, I must now accept responsibility for my own future. From now on, I make my own destiny.

It is not so much a matter of what has been given. It is what I make of it that counts. When the scales are tipped and the balance drawn, it is the deeds, thoughts and words that have made life's content that are significant.

And so, on the brink of adulthood, we will leave our incarnating child. Destiny calls and there is much ahead. He has been given the best possible start; what he makes of it is his own affair.

We wish him well, and ask a blessing for him.

Epilogue
A Personal Assessment

When the Gabriel Baby Centre was first established, there were recurring and persistent questions throughout the early years. "Is this method of child care valid for the modern child?" "Will it prepare him or her for the realities of life in the 21st Century? – or, is it too idealistic to provide a basis for life within the harshness of our technological age?"

I searched my soul over these matters, and always more questions came. "Were my ideas old-fashioned?" "Did they originate from my own childhood and not, as I imagined, from the truth of the child's being?" "Was I completely on the wrong track for today's child?"

Now, ten years further on, I have found an answer. It has come not from a study of relevant literature, nor from scientific investigation. No, it has come from another source, a human source; it is the children themselves who have provided the answer.

As the years went by and mothers returned to the Centre with their second and third child, I had an excellent opportunity to observe the older children; and this is still the case today. Moreover, I have been privileged to share in many family festivities and celebrations, and thus have been able to gain a more complete picture of these children. Many of them now attend the Melbourne Rudolf Steiner School, and from teachers I learn of their progress. I do not hear of vague dreamers, but of children capable of applying themselves whole-heartedly to the work and play of school life.

The vast majority of children, nurtured according to the ideas set out in this book, are cheerful, bright little souls, full of fun, and a joy to parents and their friends. Here there are no 'terrible two's', no need for so called 'toddler taming'. In fact, there is a noticeable lack of aggression. The answer these charming children have given me is not spoken in words, but radiated out of depths of their being and manifested in their behaviour, creative play, lively imagination and friendliness.

I do not claim any paradisical state of affairs! Of course there are the usual difficult family situations, occasional quarrels between siblings, uncertainties and sticky patches here and here. But these are incidental and leave no trace of permanent 'behaviour problems'. I personally know many delightful children who do well at school and of whom parents say, "We are lucky our daughter – or son – is so good."

This is not luck! It is a matter of parental *knowledge*, and a willingness to incorporate this into daily life. All children could be like this to a greater or lesser extent depending upon the parents' degree of understanding and application. In the long run, it is a matter of parental self-development and common-sense; it is well within the reach of all concerned people.

In preparing this book, I have called upon the knowledge and insights of many people, authorities in their own work sphere. It is a temptation to name some of the special ones here, those from whom I have gained enormously – but, where to start and where to stop? It would be impossible to decide! All of those listed in the references and bibliography have taught me something. And most of all have I gained from the unique teacher, Rudolf Steiner.

However, I hope I have had something to say which is uniquely a reflection of my own understanding of the child, gained over many years of active work and experience. If this were not so, the book would hardly have been worth the effort!

Appendix A
Rudolf Steiner

"Steiner thought, spoke, and wrote as a scientist . . . Although his own investigations carried him into fields far beyond the range of physical science, he always carried into these investigations, and into the application of them to physical phenomena, the concepts and methods of scientific thought."

Thus wrote A.P. Shepherd, a Canon of the Anglican Church, in 1954. He described Steiner well; for in the many spheres of work to which this extraordinary man gave a body of knowledge and indications for future development, the precision of his scientific thought and method of working is apparent. To describe him as a mystic or essentially a philosopher is a gross misunderstanding.

Rudolf Steiner was born in 1861. His tertiary education was received in Vienna, and he obtained his doctorate at Rostok University. In 1888 he was invited to join a team of scholars working at the Goethe Archives in Weimar, preparing a new edition of Goethe's works. Steiner was given the responsibility of preparing the scientific writings. He worked at this between 1890 and 1897, then moved to Berlin and later to Dornach in Switzerland.

Early in the 20th Century he began an intensive activity of lecturing and writing, imparting a knowledge of realms beyond the physical and man's connection with them. This occupied about twelve years, and led on to a further span of approximately six years when he was making provision for his work to be carried into the future. This entailed the formation of the Anthroposophical Society with its various working groups and eventual development of branches throughout the world.

During the last six years of his life he was active in applying his spiritual scientific knowledge to a number of activities such as agriculture, education, art, medicine, theology etc. He died in 1925, leaving a body of knowledge in many areas. This is now being applied to the practical affairs of life.

Appendix B
The Threefold Man

Rudolf Steiner has given a comprehensive outline of the threefoldness of man in his books *Theosophy* and *Occult Science*, and in many of his lectures. This threefoldness applies at all levels. The various members of man's being have been given different names by a variety of cultures from most ancient times – Indian, Persian, Greek etc. The terms used throughout this book are those used by Steiner.

First, there is the body. This is related to the three kingdoms of nature. There is a mineral structure of bones and flesh; a life-carrying element as in plants – sap (blood in animals and man); and a sentient-carrying structure as in animals – brain and nervous system.

Thus is the physical body threefold.

Furthermore, the body is not only a structure of mineral particles, but is permeated by forces of life. These also form a 'body' which penetrates the mineral, activating the particles so that there is the movement of sap and blood. Life exalts matter, and raises it to a higher level. This life-body can also be given different names; Steiner usually uses the term 'etheric body'.

So it is with the sentient forces. These too form a 'body' as they penetrate the mineral and life members. The brain and nervous system is their field of operation, and again, a higher level is reached. Soul exalts life, and for man and animal there is sensation and the feelings and impulses connected with it. Steiner calls this soul entity the 'soul-body'. Ancient literature uses the term 'astral body', and in some schools of thought it is known as the 'emotional' body.

It must not be imagined that these more subtle members of man are *products* of his brain and nervous system. They do not originate from mineral particles. Much could be said to elucidate this, but suffice it to say here that life and soul *are*. In man and animal they manifest through a mineral body, enlivening, and bringing the possibility of sensation to what otherwise must remain inert and non-sentient.

A threefoldness is also observable in the soul. This is set out in Chapters Twelve and Fifteen. There are the three soul functions of will, feeling and thinking; and the 'constitution' of the soul itself consists of an experiencing or sentient member, the intellect or rational mind, and a higher member which gives the possibility of access to the realm of spirit.

Thus, while the phenomenal world presents as a duality – long short, high low, hot cold – it will be seen that man is essentially a trinity. He is truly made in the image of God.

Appendix C
The Forty Days Period

Amongst the ancient myths of many peoples, there is to be found the story of a great deluge. In the Christian Bible it is portrayed as the great flood associated with Noah and the ark. We are told that it rained for forty days and forty nights, and, that on the fortieth day Noah opened the window of the ark.

Rudolf Steiner has given much to elucidate this. In his book *Occult Science* he describes a number of immense epochs of evolution each of which enabled mankind to develop a specific state of consciousness. Between each of these epochs there occurred a major happening which caused the transition to the succeeding period. The story of the flood portrays one such major happening. This gave the possibility for mankind to take a further step forward, attaining thereby a greater clarity of consciousness.

Emil Bock's book *Genesis* further illuminates the story. He describes Noah as the same being as Manu, the great initiate who, according to ancient literature, led his people from west to east to establish a new culture. Through this transition, mankind underwent adaption to new conditions, thereby gaining new opportunities.

In the New Testament, Christ, after the baptism retired into the desert wilderness for forty days. To gain even a little understanding of the deeply esoteric events surrounding the life of Christ demands years of study and reflection. Again, Rudolf Steiner brings light to bear on many of these profound mysteries.

For our purpose it is enough to note that after the immensely significant happening at the Jordan, Christ withdrew from the hurly-burly of life, retiring into seclusion to adapt himself to a new state of being. Again, forty days were needed to establish this.

The incarnation of the human spirit requires similar periods of adaption as has been shown in the text; first from the spiritual to the physical, then from the watery to the air-earthy. The first of these is in the hands of the gods; the second, in the hands of the parents. Both are crucial to the well-being of the human spirit.

Appendix D
Life-Forces and Food

In his book *Theosophy*, Rudolf Steiner speaks of an undifferentiated "ocean of life", which he describes as the primal source of all life on earth. Here in the world, this life manifests through the myriads of different forms that make up the organic kingdoms.

As was stated in Appendix B, life is not a product of matter, but uses the mineral for its manifestation on earth. In the organic world, there is a mineral structure governed by inorganic laws, and in addition, there are activating forces of life governed by their own laws (See Appendix J).

In foods, including milk and honey, it is the vitality of these life-forces which nourish; and in organisms such as fruits and vegetables there can be maximum life or minimum life according to the condition of the soil and method of fertilization.

The quality of vital forces of milk depends on the method of fertilization of the pasture on which the cows have grazed, and the subsequent handling of the milk.

Honey is also a living food. Dr Eugen and Lilly Kolisko dedicated many years of research to it, and found it to contain an abundance and variety of formative forces. (*Agriculture of Tomorrow* by Dr Eugen & Lilly Kolisko. Kolisko Archive, Bournemouth, U.K.)

From Rudolf Steiner's lectures on agriculture given in 1924 we learn " . . . the greater part of what we daily eat is not there to be received as *substance* into the body . . . (It) is there to give the body the *forces* which it contains, and to call forth in the body mobility and activity."

Therefore it can be said that the food value of a product containing living forces is much more than the summation of its chemical constituents.

The quality of these life forces can be tested by a science which has learned to read the "very real script which Nature places before our eyes." (*Agriculture of Tomorrow*) In their book *Agriculture of Tomorrow*, the Koliskos state, " . . . We have developed a specific method of research which enables us to find the various *forces* hidden in the substances, just as vitamins are hidden in fresh vegetables and fruit. We call our method capillary Dynamolysis." (Part II. Section XVIII)

It is in these new directions of research that the answer to nutrition lies, and this includes a life-imbued infant feeding.

Appendix E
Music for Young Children

Lullabies and songs for young children by courtesy of Joseph Mani.

Good mor-ning gol-den sun - shine,
The birds fly out and sing so gay,

m - m - m - m - m - m - m - m
du - du - du - du - du - du - du - du

you're look-ing through my win-dow fine.
and thank the Lord for this fine day.

Alois Künstler

O Angel Mine

O An-gel mine, pro-tect me fine,

night and day , ear-ly and late

till my soul en-ters the hea-ven-ly shine.

O An-gel mine, pro-tect me fine.

Alois Künstler

Sleep Baby, Sleep

Sleep Ba - by , sleep , thy

fath - er tends the sheep, thy

moth - er shakes the dream-land-tree,

down fall the lit - tle dreams for thee,

sleep ba - by sleep.

Traditional

Cradle Song

Lul - la - by and good-night with
lul - la - by and good-night let

li - lies of white and ro-ses of
an - gels of light spread wings round your

red, to pil - low your head, may you
bed and guard you from dread, slumber

wake when the day cha-ses dark-ness a-
gen - tly and deep in the dream-land of

way, may you wake when the day cha-ses
sleep, slumber gen-tly and deep, in the

dark - ness a - way.
dream - land of sleep.

Johannes Brahms

Appendix F
The Continuum Concept

Jean Liedloff, in her book *The Continuum Concept* advocates what she calls an 'in-arms phase' which should extend "between birth and the voluntary commencement of crawling". That is, the infant should be continually carried by the mother during this time.

While much in her book is admirable and sensitive, it is based on a number of false premises. One of these is her assumption that what is beneficial for a child born into a tribal consciousness is also suitable for a child born into a 20th Century consciousness.

This is absolutely not so, for the consciousness of man has evolved and developed over the ages. Each stage has given new possibilities for developing individuality and freedom. The modern child in his consciousness is a totally different being from the tribal child, and needs totally different challenges and experiences. (See the section on 'Weaning' in Chapter Ten.)

Also, a statement such as "Mother in a bed three feet away . . . could as well be on Mars", shows a complete lack of understanding of the soul and spiritual bond existing between mother and child. This is not dependent on space. The mother's soul warmth (see 'Madonna's Cloak' in Chapter Thirteen) continually flows about the baby wherever he is, and there is a very real connection at this level.

A further comment could be made about the gentle rhythmical walk of some women in the third world. I was able to observe this while in India. Such a rhythm would indeed soothe the baby. It is very different in our culture, where mother rushes to answer the phone, hurries back to the kitchen to see that the dinner is not burning, or runs out to the laundry to see if she has left the iron on. These hurried and often anxious-filled movements are anything but calm and rhythmical, and can only be disturbing for the child. He would be in a much calmer atmosphere in his bassinet or cradle in a sheltered spot in the garden, or in a quiet room indoors – and still be in touch with Mother on the soul level.

One must also consider the mechanical noises already referred to in the modern home, and compare these with the quiet of the rural environment of the Yequana tribe, on whose life-style Jean Liedloff based her ideas.

Appendix G
How to Make and Tie a Rebozo

By courtesy of The Nursing Mothers' Association of Australia.

How to Make Your Rebozo

The eye-catching Mexican Rebozo is usually hand-woven in two or more colours, from wool or cotton of various weights and weaves. But it isn't necessary to weave *your* Rebozo! A length of strong, soft, washable cotton or light weight woollen fabric will be just as effective.

All you need is a piece about 2.25 metres long by 0.75 to 0.9 metres wide (2½ – 3 yards long by 30 to 36 inches wide).

First of all: Straighten the fabric by pulling a thread along each raw edge and trimming along the thread 'track'.

To fringe the ends. Decide the depth of fringe you want and pull another thread at that depth, using a pin or strong needle to lift it out. Machine stitch just above the new 'track'. A zig-zag attachment is useful for this. Pull out all crosswise threads from the bottom up to zig-zag stitching.

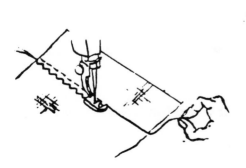
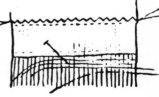

How to Tie Your Rebozo

Step 1.
Spread the Rebozo to its full width across your arms and shoulders, shorter on the side where baby's head will lie. (Side A)

Step 2.
Place baby along, not across, the outside of the shorter side. (Side A)

Step 3.
Fold side edges of Side A over baby, with fringed edge hanging over his feet.

Step 4.
Fold fringed ends loosely under or over baby's feet and secure with safety pin.

Step 5.
Hold the longer side (Side B) away from you, and lay it over baby.

Step 6.
Tuck Side B under baby, pulling fringed end up as far as it will come between baby and your breast, to wrap him snugly. The rest of Side B can now be laid over and tucked around baby on the side away from your body, between.Sides A and B.

Step 7.
Now your baby is snug and your arms are free. If you are a beginner, you may prefer to keep one arm under baby to be sure or even pop in a couple of large safety pins.

Appendix H
Rhythm in Nutrition

The importance of rhythm in nutrition is highly underestimated. The necessity for a rhythmic pattern in nutrition applies to all people of whatever age, and it is especially important to establish this early in life starting with the breast feeding of the infant.

In his book *The Dynamics of Nutrition*, Gerhard Schmidt devotes a whole chapter to this important subject. "For man in older times, it was an archetypal experience that all life in humans, in the earth and in the cosmos was permeated by rhythms. Man lived with these rhythms during the course of the year and the day." And he reminds us that Steiner pointed directly to the central concern of rhythm in nutrition.

"What actually is digestive activity? It is a metabolic activity which unfolds itself towards the rhythmical. Digestive activity is metabolic activity taken up by the rhythm of the circulatory organs.

"We can readily say that the essence of nutrition lies in the activity of taking up nutriments into man's inner rhythm."

Schmidt develops his theme by talking of the rhythms of various organs; for example, "the 24 hour rhythm of the liver". He concludes the chapter with a section on "The significance of Rhythm for Human Health", and observes that "Man now faces the task of becoming the creator of his own individual rhythm, of reuniting himself with the great world rhythms."

The above thoughts and observations of Schmidt can be a stimulus to us all to regulate our life more rhythmically. This is of particular importance for the young infant and growing child if he is to live in harmony and health with the rhythms of his own body and of the cosmos. It applies to breast feeding, the preparation and serving of meals and the child's daily pattern.

We have discussed it more fully in Chapter Eleven.

Appendix I
Weaning

The Consciousness of the Group and of the Individual

To gain an understanding of why prolonged breast feeding goes beyond 'bonding' and tends towards 'binding' requires first an understanding of the threefold man as set out in Appendix B. We have spoken of man's three 'bodies' – one of physical matter, a second made up of life forces, and a third of soul forces. These are observable realities for those able to see beyond the material.

Each of these bodies carries part of our being. For instance, the soul body carries our personal characteristics – that is, our personality, which is part of our soul life. On the other hand, our physical body reveals our racial characteristics. A Chinese, Zulu, European, Eskimo and Amerindian all have distinctly different bodily features. These are unmistakably marked upon the physical body.

Then, we also have other characteristics which belong to our nation or folk or tribe. There is the reserve of the English, the romantic nature of the Italians, and the out-goingness of the Australians. These are more deep-seated and permanent than are the personal joys and sorrows of the soul. Our folk characteristics are those of the whole nation, and it is these that are carried in the life body.

It may now well be asked, "What has all this to do with breast feeding and weaning?"

It is the forces from the mother's life body, abundant in her milk, that flow over to the child in breast feeding, for milk is a living food (see Appendix D) – it is permeated through and through by forces of life. Strange as it may seem, it is these life forces carrying the national (or tribal) characteristics which help bond the child to mother and family, and help him fit into a certain national pattern. It could be said that the characteristics of the nation are stamped upon the child by the life forces in the mother's milk. This is yet another tremendous advantage of breast feeding; the child is prepared to feel at home within his cultural background.

However, if these family and national characteristics are accentuated and very strongly stamped upon the child – and this is what prolonged breast feeding does – it could be a hindrance to the later gaining of a strong sense of one's own individuality, so necessary for our modern consciousness.

Hence, prolonged breast feeding ideally prepares the child for the group consciousness – it binds to the tribe. But . . "one questions its wisdom for the modern child".

Appendix J
Matter and Life

A little over ten years ago, two important publications appeared in Europe, both by professors of pure physics – *Nature and the Godly* by Walter Heitler (Zug, 1974), and *Cul-de-sac Faith of Science* by Max Thurkauf (Zurich, 1975). Both are concerned with the question of the origin of life and its relationship to matter; and both are critical of the 'mechanistic-deterministic approach' of natural science (Thurkauf).

More recently another book on the same subject has cause a furore amongst scientists. It is Dr Rupert Sheldrake's *A New Science of Life*. This also questions the assumption "that living organisms are nothing but complex machines, governed by the known laws of physics and chemistry." After an exhaustive argument, examining all possibilities, Sheldrake arrives at the possibility of "the reality of a transcendent source of the universe."

The two physicists mentioned above are equally sceptical of the scientific dogma that the origin of life is to be found in the mineral particle. In defining the credo of what he calls a "dialectic materialism" Thurkauf makes the following criticism. Dialectic materialism considers that "life is the sum of physics and chemistry, i.e. a machine. Machines are makeable, consequently life (and thus everything) is makeable". He points out that it is the realm of "the precise physical experiment . . . where a subject-object division is given" which is the true realm of the exact sciences; then goes on to say, "In the realm of biology however, only a morphological observing-thinking is adequate."

He pursues his theme by examining a fundamental difference between matter and life. "The modern scientific outlook is able to analyse the world into infinitesimal elements . . . (But) life always appears in wholes. That is one reason why all efforts to find a life differential (that is, the 'atoms' of life) are quite in vain. Life is that which vanishes in the test tube." (M. Thurkauf, Erwin Chargaff and Linus Pauling).

Heitler is equally concerned to show that life is not produced by matter. In reviewing his work, Lore Deggeller* says "Heitler tries to release science from its preoccupation with only physico-chemical processes by indicating that through precisely the specific life process, physical and chemical laws are partly repressed (reference is made to osmosis and capillarity where water arises against gravity) 'The life-laws subordinate the laws of the lifeless – i.e. the laws of physics. There is obviously a hierarchical ordering of laws and forces whose second stage is represented by a vegetative life'."

Various other observations are made, and then Heitler makes the following almost epoch-making statement. "Life is not a complex fulfilment of the laws of physics and chemistry, but rather is their antithesis." (page 58). Surely this has a revolutionary ring worthy of a Copernicus or Kepler!

To apply these statements to milk formulae for infants "demands the courage to explore new dimensions of knowledge." Let us hope that those concerned with this question, so vitally important for the infant, will take note!

---

* I am greatly indebted to Lore Deggeller's review of Heitler's and Thurkauf's books, published under the title *The Dogma of Materialism - an effort in overcoming it in physics*. I have used her review extensively for this Appendix.

Appendix K
Man and Plant

Rudolf Steiner described the plant as an "upside down man". There is a relationship between the root and our head-sensory organization, for with the root the plant 'senses out' for the nutrients of the soil; it is the brain of the plant.

The middle region, the leaves, is related to our respiratory system, for through the leaves the plant breathes. And the blossom, from which the seed forms, is obviously related to our system of reproduction. It can also be considered in relation to our digestive system, for through the bees, a sort of digesting goes on in the flower.

Thus, for children who are all 'head', the alert quick learners whose intellectual capacities stir too early, the blossoms and leaves bring a harmony. Dr Grethe Hauschka comments*, "In such a case one does well to emphasize the sweet and aromatic blossom element in a child's diet. He should be given milk for a longer period to keep cosmic forces working plastically on his organism, and have plenty of leafy vegetables to help his rhythmic system get well rounded." She makes the following interesting observation about these children. "It is very important to see that such children work a lot with colour and form and are constantly encouraged to live in the imaginative element."*

The dreamy-eyed idealists, those sensitive children who ask for patience and gentleness from parents, are helped to sense into the world more strongly by roots. Dr Hauschka describes these children as "little dreamers who find it hard to loosen their ties with their pre-earthly paradise."*

* Rudolf Hauschka, *Nutrition*

Appendix L
Head Growth of Children

Published by courtesy of the National Health and Medical Research
Council, Commonwealth of Australia.

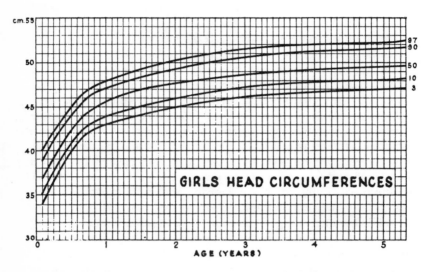

GIRLS HEAD CIRCUMFERENCES

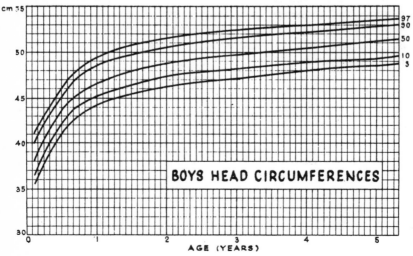

BOYS HEAD CIRCUMFERENCES

Appendix M
How to Knit a Pony

Use any ply wool on suitable needles – pure wool in natural colours is best.

Cast on 38 stitches. Commence and work 12 rows of garter stitch (plain knitting, knit each row). These are the back legs.

Cast off 12 stitches each side for body. Knit 12 rows.

Cast on 12 stitches each side (front legs)

Next row: cast on 11 stitches in centre (creates hole)

Knit on, increasing 1 stitch on either side of centre.

Increase every 3rd row for 12 rows (4 incs).

Now cast off 21 stitches each side, knit 1 row.

Next row cast on 3 stitches at each end, then 2 stitches at each end of next row.

Knit 6 rows for head.

Cast off.

Stitch together and stuff with pure unspun fleece.

Sew mane in hole in neck.

Put on tail.

I am grateful to the Blue Mountains Waldorf School for giving me permission to use this. It was first published in their March 1985 Newsletter.

Notes and References

Foreword

1. The Gabriel Baby Centre is a private practice in maternal and child welfare, founded in Melbourne in 1976 by Joan Salter who is its present Director. The basis of its work is the outline of man given by Rudolf Steiner earlier this century (see Appendix B). Joan Salter is a specialist in maternal and child care, and has a nursing background.

2. The term 'Spiritual Science' used by Steiner may seem a contradiction to those for whom 'science' denotes an activity of investigation on the physical plane; that is, a natural science. This latter involves objectivity of investigation and proof.

    Steiner, using the powers of his soul (rather than microscope and test tube) was able to investigate realms beyond the physical with equal objectivity – hence his justification for the term 'Spiritual Science'. He describes the gradual development of this unusual capacity in his autobiography.

    Having grasped and understood what he actually perceived in these non-spatial realms, Steiner was then able to present it in thought forms suitable for present-day consciousness. This is a totally different approach from a subjective mysticism. Steiner rejected the latter, and considered it inappropriate for our scientific age, and, indeed, fraught with dangers and the possibility of error.

Chapter One

1. The following figures, supplied by the Australian Commonwealth Bureau of Statistics, show the dramatic fall in the infant mortality rate over a period of 73 years. The figures indicate the number of infants who died in the first year of life per thousand live births.

For the year ending December	Victoria	Australia
1910	76.8	74.81
1981	9.4	10.3
1982	10.7	10
1983	8.9	9.4

Chapter Two

1. *Intimations of Immortality*, W. Wordsworth.

2. From the book *Towards Self Development*, T. S. Hughes.

3. *Intimations of Immortality*, W. Wordsworth.

4. *Embryology and World Evolution*, a series of lectures given by Dr Karl König between 15th October 1965 and 13th March 1966.

5. See Dr Hermann Poppelbaum, *Man and Animal*, Anthroposophical Publishing Company, London 1960.

6. Stanley Drake, *A Path to Birth*. Floris Books, Edinburgh, 1979.

Chapter Three

1. W. zur Linden, *A Child is Born*. Wilhelm zur Linden was a German paediatrician. His book *A Child is Born* is his major published contribution to child care.

2. Some years ago, an excellent article written by Beverley Lane was published in the newsletter of Childbirth Education Association, Victoria, Australia. I have called on it freely for this section, and wish to acknowledge my indebtedness to the author.

3. Norbert Glas, *Conception Birth and Early Childhood*, Anthroposophic Press, Spring Valley, NY, 1984.

4. W. zur Linden, *A Child is Born*.

5. Virginia Phillips, *Successful Breast Feeding*.

6. Ibid.

7. Ashley Montague, *Touching*.

8. 'Weleda' is a company which manufactures toiletries and medicines according to principles laid down by Rudolf Steiner. Its headquarters is in Arlesheim, Switzerland.

9. Dr Otto Wolff has published a considerable volume of books, pamphlets and articles on a medical point of view which was indicated by Rudolf Steiner and further developed by Dr Ita Wegman. This is usually referred to as 'Anthroposophical medicine'. Dr Wolff's small booklet *Anthroposophically Orientated Medicine and its Remedies* (Weleda, Arlesheim, Switzerland, 1977) sets this out very briefly and is a good introduction.

10. Gladys Mayer, *The Mystery Wisdom of Colour*.
    Hilde Boos-Hamburger, *The Creative Power of Colour*.

Rudolf Steiner, *Colour*.

The above books do not deal specifically with colour for children. They give a picture of the deeper meaning of the colours and suggest painting exercises which help towards an understanding of them.

11. Gladys Mayer, 1888 to 1980, was a contemporary of Rudolf Steiner and knew him personally. She lived in London where she founded the Mercury Arts Group. She wrote of Steiner as "the Great Initiate who lived amongst us, and to whom we were privileged to speak." During a stay in London in 1973, I had the equally great privilege of meeting this most remarkable woman.

Chapter Four

1. Here I have used descriptions given me by mothers attending the Gabriel Baby Centre.

2. See the Gospel of St Luke, chapter 10 verse 20.

Chapter Five

1. The book *Lifeways,* edited by Gudrun Davy and Bons Voors, contains excellent descriptions of the experience of motherhood and family life. It is written by a number of women whose quest for meaning and freedom within family life brought them to a conscious looking at the phenomenon of motherhood.

2. From Norbert Glas, *Conception Birth and Early Childhood,* Anthroposophic Press, Spring Valley, NY, 1984.

Chapter Six

1. For many years I conducted Maternal and child Welfare Services in Migrant Hostels in Victoria, and was fortunate to be able to observe many of these wisdom-filled old customs practised by unsophisticated people.

2. In Rudolf Steiner curative homes, the lyre is used for its calming effect and the flute is often played first thing in the morning to indicate time for rising.

3. Ashley Montague, *Touching,* op. cit.

4. Amelia Auckett, *Baby Massage,* Newmarket, NY, 1982. Massage can also be used for some babies with anatomical abnormalities. Dr Margaretha Hauschka states "massage treatment with all rachitic deformities has been successful, also treatment of other curvatures and obstructions of growth in the limbs, which often have an interuterine origin" *Rhythmical Massage.* These, of course, are medical cases, and massage should only be

given under the supervision of a doctor skilled in this area of medicine.

5. Hauschka ibid. "Warmth is the bridge between the sensory and supersensory worlds, it stands on the boundary between the material and spiritual worlds…Thus the warmth organism is of a significance that is tremendous, though not easily assessed."

Chapter Seven

1. Rudolf Steiner, *Man as Symphony of the Creative Word*, a series of lectures given by Rudolf Steiner in 1923. "…man in his whole structure, in the conditions of his life, indeed in all that he is, presents a Little World, a microcosm over against the macrocosm: he actually contains within himself all the laws, all the secrets of the world."

2. In her book *A Land*, Jacquetta Hawkes sets out a Geological Time Scale; and Hermann Poppelbaum in his book *Man and Animal* gives a diagram of "Physical Evolution Ascending and Spiritual Evolution Descending." In this chapter I have used both of these for reference.

3. In his book *Occult Science - An Outline*, Rudolf Steiner describes the evolutionary process of our universe. He traces man's development from a primal spiritual state of being, a "living in the bosom of the Gods", to an independent man living in a mineral body on earth, fully conscious of himself. On all levels, the child is a microcosm of this development of humanity.

4. Joan Beck, *How to Raise a Brighter Child*, USA, 1984.

5. See the composite table compiled from Dr Mary Sheridan's Child Development Tables, and the Denver Chart set out in the 8th edition of *A Guide to the Care of the Young Child*, published by the Department of Health, Victoria, Australia 1976.
   It lists a child of two months as follows: "Prone: Head held off table intermittently." And at four months, "Prone: swimming movements with arms."
   In his book *How a Baby Grows* Dr Arnold Gesell who founded The Clinic of Child Development at Yale University in 1911, and became its Director, shows a photograph of a four-month-old baby with the caption "A 16-weeks-old baby tries 'swimming' on the floor".

6. In his book *The First Three Years of the Child*, Dr Karl König points to the well-recognised fact that "It is possible to induce walking movements in all normal healthy new-born babies." However the faculty is later lost, and has to be regained through the child's own will activity. König goes on to say, "during the second quarter of the (first) year, a *readiness* to stand occurs…" It is this latter activity which points to the striving of the ego. The former was merely a reflex action.

7. Dr Karl König (op. cit.) sets out this sequence of development as follows: "The head is the first member to withdraw from chaotic movement. Chest and arms are pulled along after it, and finally the legs and feet extricate themselves. This process seems to be patterned after that of actual birth. Just as in birth the head is the first part of the body to emerge and is gradually followed by the rest of the body, so here, out of the uterus of dissociated movements, co-ordinated movement is born and orientated step by step towards standing and walking. At the end of the first year the process of the birth of movement is completed."

8. Walkers adversely affect the posture of a child. For example, it has been found that some children begin to walk on their toes after having been constantly in a walker.

On the soul level, an inhibition of the sense of freedom, and restriction of will forces in infancy could manifest in adult life as ineptitude in various areas such as work application, a capacity to 'flow out' freely into life in friendships and other relationships. That is, it could result in a feeling of always being restricted.

9. Norbert Glas op. cit.

10. "The consciousness of man's ancestor had previously been dreamlike. Now, through the erect posture...the ground was prepared for the consciousness proper to the earth period." Hermann Poppelbaum op. cit.

11. Rudolf Steiner *Occult Science - an Outline*, Rudolf Steiner Press, London, 1969.

Chapter Eight

1. It could be thought that animals also create. But the bird builds its nest from instinct; it is not a thinking and conscious activity. This applies to all animals, and however wonderful and wisdom-filled their activities are, they are not imbued with a creative consciousness. This is a fundamental difference between animal and man. The mammal on its four feet is anchored inexorably to the earth. It is not made in the image of God.

Chapter Nine

1. Wolfgang Schad "Notes on the Study of Man". This forms an appendix to the book *Understanding Children's Drawings* by Michaela Strauss.

2. *Understanding Children's Drawings* by Michaela Strauss, daughter of Hanns Strauss (see note 3). She is connected with Rudolf Steiner pedagogy.

3. Hanns Strauss was a painter who lived in Munich earlier this century. From 1923 onwards he was connected with Rudolf Steiner pedagogy in

Germany, and when the Steiner schools were closed by the Nazi regime, he undertook lecture tours to groups of the 'Fellowship for Freedom in Education'. It was in the later 1920's that he began to collect the drawings of young children and amassed a collection of about 6000 pictures. These, and a collection of his notes are the main source of his daughter's book.

4. Michaela Strauss *Understanding Children's Drawings*.

5. Ibid.

6. Ibid.

7. Ibid.

8. Ibid.

9. Ibid.

10. Ibid.

11. Ibid.

12. Ibid.

Chapter Ten

1. See Rudolf Steiner *Theosophy*, Rudolf Steiner Press, London, 1965.

2. Rudolf Hauschka *Nutrition*. Rudolf Steiner Press, London, 1967. The book also contains an addendum written by the author's wife Dr Grethe (Margarethe) Hauschka, a section of which deals with "Nutrition in Childhood and Youth".

3. Scientists are now discovering the uniqueness of the chemical composition of breast milk – see the publication "The Uniqueness of Breast Milk" edited by D. B. Jelliffe and E. F. P. Jelliffe, *The American Journal of Clinical Nutrition*, volume 24, August 1971.

4. Carl Jung *Modern Man in Search of a Soul*. "I freely admit that this problem of feeling has been one over which I have racked my brains."

5. Daisy Bates *The Passing of the Aborigines*. Putnam, London, 1938. "...I learned the admirable nature system, based wholly on legend and tradition, and implicitly obeyed...Breaches of totemic and marriage laws were capital crimes. Theft was unknown, because individual ownership was unknown..."

6. See *The Gospel of St John*, twelve lectures given by Rudolf Steiner at

Hamburg, from May 18th to 31st 1908, Anthroposophical Press, New York 1962.

7. It must be stressed that these occasions *are* very rare. Almost all mothers can perform this natural feeding function if there is a real desire to do so. Virginia Phillips in her book *Successful Breast Feeding* says "Biological reasons for being unable to breast feed are very few, and the vast majority of women can breast feed with success if they really desire to, and have cultural support." That has certainly been my experience over many years of work in this field.

8. Reported by Dr E.E.Pfeiffer in an article reprinted as a 'Special Report' by the Natural Food Associates, Atlanta, Texas (p.1, revised edition).

9. Ibid.

10. Ibid.

11. Ibid.

12. The fact that babies "put everything into their mouth" a good deal earlier than this does not indicate that they need extra food. The baby has a strong instinct to suck, and furthermore, the lips are a most sensitive organ of touch. Therefore, the infant explores objects by attempting to suck them. This has nothing to do with nutritional needs or hunger.

13. Rudolf Steiner *Nine Lectures on Bees*, St George Publications, New York, 1975.

14. Rudolf Hauschka *Nutrition*.

15. *A Guide to the Care of the Young Child* published by the Health Commission of Victoria, Australia 1976, recommends 700 to 900ml of milk daily for the one to two-year-old child, and 750 to 900ml for three to five years old. This includes *all* milk including yoghourt etc., not only that which the child drinks. In practice it means two or three cups of milk a day, milk with the morning cereal, and some yoghourt or cheese a few times a week. Milk can also be given in soups.

16. Rudolf Steiner has given many lectures on the deep mysteries associated with Easter.

17. Rudolf Steiner *Man as a Symphony of the Creative Word*.

18. Ibid.

19. Gerhardt Schmidt in his book *The Dynamics of Nutrition* gives a section on milk and milk products, and explains why this is so.

20. *Agriculture of Tomorrow*, Dr Eugen and Lilly Kolosko. See also Appendix D.

21. Rudolf Hauschka *Nutrition*.

22. The seed of the legume contains 25% protein compared to grains which have 10%.

23. See *Dynamics of Nutrition* by Gerhardt Schmidt.

24. John Bowlby *Child Care and the Growth of Love*, Penguin, London, 1951.

25. *Clinical Nutrition* 1968 and *Nutritional Review* 1967. It is significant that breast milk has a modest sodium content (7m Eq/litre).

Chapter Eleven

1. Willi Aeppli in his book *The Care and Development of the Human Senses* presents a detailed and comprehensive study of this subject.

2. Ibid.

3. Ashley Montague *Touching*.

4. See *A Child is Born* Wilhelm Zur Linden.

5. So many studies have been done on the effects of television on children that only a few names can be mentioned here – e.g. Marie Winn *The Plug-In Drug;* Fred and Merrlyn Emery *A Choice of Futures* (The Centre for Continuing Education, Australian National University, Canberra); Jerry Mander *Four Arguments for the Elimination of Television* (William Morrow & Co.); John Ott *Health and Light* (Pocket Books). So extensive is the literature on this subject, that I have had perforce to limit myself. I have used almost exclusively the book *Who's Bringing Them Up?* by Martin Large, Hawthorn Press, 1981.

6. John Ott *Health and Light*.

7. From the book *Who's Bringing Them Up?* by Martin Large.

8. Ibid.

9. Published 1975.

10. Ibid.

11. Martin Large op. cit.

12. Ibid.

13. Reported in the paper *Community Health,* volume 9, no. 4, 1978. From Martin Large op. cit.

14. I have had the good fortune of working in several kindergartens, and have been able to observe this myself.

15. Paper published in *Newsweek* 1977. From Martin Large op. cit.

16. Joseph Chilton Pearce *The Magical Child,* Bantam, New York, 1980.

17. Ibid.

18. Janine Lévy *Exercises for your Baby.*

19. Ibid.

20. Ibid.

21. Ibid.

22. Norbert Glas *Conception Birth and Early Childhood.*

23. Ibid.

24. Eurythmy is an art of movement developed by Rudolf Steiner who described it as speech made visible. There is an artistic, a hygienic and a curative form. It is practised in all Steiner schools and healing institutions.

25. Pentatonic songs are excellent for the kindergarten years. Elizabeth Lebret has compiled an excellent collection of these. For the older child, *A Book of Songs* by Walter Braithwaite can be highly recommended. Yehudi Menuhin in a foreword describes it as being a collection of "charming and beautiful songs (which) have provided many years' sustenance and inspiration to school-children...This set of songs ...feeds the child's deep and imperative spiritual needs."

Chapter Twelve

1. See *Better Late than Early,* by Raymond S. Moore and Dorothy W. Moore, Chapter 7. They state "studies have demonstrated a variety of significant changes in brain maturation between ages 7 and 11." They quote Dr David Metcalf of the University of Colorado Medical School who "believes that the division of labour between the two sides (i.e. the two hemispheres of the brain) is probably established somewhere between 7 and 9 years of age."

2. A. C. Harwood *The Way of a Child*. The author was involved in Rudolf Steiner pedagogy in the UK for many years. He has written a number of books on the subject.

3. Ibid.

4. See the Moores op. cit., Chapter 8. Here they quote a number of authorities including Piaget to substantiate their statement "The 'wisdom' of forcing a child's intellect has little basis either in research or in common sense... To take a child through the experience of reading when he cannot exercise reasoning is an exercise in futility."

5. Picture thinking does not develop from being shown a lot of pictures. It wells up *within* the child, in his imagination. It is not dependent on *outwardly* looking at pictures.

Chapter Thirteen

1. Joseph Chilton Pearce in his book *The Magical Child* recognises this reality. He expresses it thus: "The truth is, the fully conscious parent encompasses the psychological state of the child. They participate in shared functions that need no articulation, that simply call for spontaneous response, a mutual meeting of needs and a mutual fulfilment on emotional-intuitive levels."

2. See *Education Towards Freedom* by Frans Carlgren, Lanthorn Press, East Grinstead, Sussex, UK, 1976.

3. See *At the Gates of Spiritual Science* by Rudolf Steiner – a lecture given in August 1906. Rudolf Steiner Press, London, 1970.

4. Norbert Glas *Conception Birth and Early Childhood*.

5. Ibid.

6. For this section I have called on Ursula Grahl's wonderful small book *The Wisdom in Fairy Tales*. New Knowledge Books, East Grinstead, Sussex, UK.

7. Ibid.

8. Ibid.

9. Ibid.

10. See *Popular Nursery Rhymes* edited by J. Mulherin. This is an excellent book which gives the complete rhyme and its historical background. Published by Granada.

11. I am grateful to Rani Petherbridge for giving me permission to use this. It was first published in the Little Yarra Steiner School Newsletter, midwinter 1985.

12. John Bowlby *Child Care and the Growth of Love* – a summary of a report prepared under the auspices of W.H.O. in 1951.

13. Ibid. Bowlby's findings substantiate this.

14. Ibid.

15. The Victorian Institute of Family Studies is a fertile field of information on this subject.

16. Judith Wallerstein: Paper presented at the annual meeting of the Orthopsychiatric Association, Toronto, 1984.

17. *A Child's Eye-View of Family Life:* Report of a study conducted in Victoria 1982-83, compiled by Gay Ochiltree and Paul Amato. Published April 1985 by the Victorian Institute of Family Studies.

18. Judith Wallerstein op. cit.

19. I personally know a number of such families and have had the privilege of sharing many of their family festivities – birthday celebrations, baptisms, Christmas and so on. It is largely out of these experiences that I have been able to write this section on family life.

Chapter Fourteen

1. D. W. Winnicott *The Child, the Family and the Outside World*. Tavistock, London, 1964.

2. See authorities such as Professor Jolly, Dr Raymond Moore, Dorothy Moore, Dr Benjamin Spock and many others. Also, publications by the Nursing Mothers' Association of Australia such as their booklet *Understanding Wakeful Babies*, and their newsletter of August 1983, *Living With Babies Whose Time-clocks Are Out*.

3. Hugh Jolly *Book of Child Care*. Allen & Unwin, London, 1985.

4. See *The Case against Immunization* by Richard Moskowitz. He is a medical practitioner who has studied homeopathy. Article in 'Mothering' Spring 1984. Booklet available from The National Centre for Homeopathy, 1500 Massachusetts Avenue, NW Washington DC, 20005, USA.

5. I have seen two such children myself.

6. See letter from the Commonwealth Serum Laboratories Melbourne to the Gabriel Baby Centre, dated 24th June 1985.

7. See *Every Second Child* by Archie Kalokerinos. Keats Pub. Inc., 1986.

8. Richard Moskowitz op. cit.

9. See data available from the Australian Bureau of Statistics, Melbourne.

10. Letter from the Royal Children's Hospital, Melbourne to the Gabriel Baby Centre, dated 18th June 1980.

11. Richard Moskowitz op. cit.

12. See data available from the Commonwealth Serum Laboratories Melbourne.

13. Moore op. cit. Reader's Digest Press, New York, 1975. Dr Moore is a developmental psychologist and has held a number of senior positions in education.

14. Ibid.

15. Lady Gowrie Centres throughout Australia could be described as model kindergartens concerned with pre-school programmes, research, and teaching. The report referred to is one of their many publications.

16. Ibid.

17. Ibid.

18. Ibid.

19. I know several families where this is the case. It is also the opinion of Nimnicht who at one time was principal psychologist for Head Start in USA. He says "There is no evidence that a young child needs to go to nursery school." (Quoted from Moore op. cit.)

20. Maria Montessori *The Secret of Childhood*.

21. Ibid.

22. Ibid.

23. Dr Rudolf Dreikurs, an eminent American psychologist has written an excellent book called *Happy Children*, (Fontana) in which he deals with child behaviour. The titles of two of the chapters indicate his theme – Chapter 7, "Be Firm without Dominating"; Chapter 20, "Use Care in

Pleasing: Have the Courage to Say No". The book is highly recommended.

24. *Piaget's Theory of Intellectual Development - an Introduction* by Herbert Ginsberg and Sylvia Opper.

25. Karl König *The First Three Years of the Child*.

26. See *Cosmic Memory* by Rudolf Steiner. Harper and Row, San Francisco, 1981.

27. Karl König op. cit.

28. Rudolf Steiner *Theosophy*.

29. *Human Values in Education*. Ten lectures given by Rudolf Steiner in July 1924. Anthroposophic Press, New York, 1969.

30. Ibid.

Chapter Fifteen

1. Karl König *The Human Soul*. Anthroposophic Press, New York, 1973.

2. Rudolf Steiner *Theosophy*.

3. Ibid.

4. Ibid.

5. Ibid.

6. See *The Age* newspaper, Melbourne 14th May 1985. It states "a recent study by the Bureau of Statistics shows an 11% increase in suicides amongst young males between the ages of 15 and 24, in the four years to 1982…The increase in the suicide rate is a trend in the Western world."

7. Rudolf Steiner *Theosophy*.

8. Ibid.

Chapter Sixteen

1. Rudolf Steiner *Theosophy*.

2. Ibid.

3. Ibid.

4. Ibid.

5. Ibid.

6. Ginsberg and Opper op. cit. Prentice Hall Inc., New Jersey, 1969.

7. Ibid.

8. Ibid.

9. Ibid.

10. Ibid.

11. Reported in *The Age* newspaper, Melbourne May 23rd 1985.

12. Ginsburg and Opper op. cit.

13. Ibid.

Chapter Seventeen

1. See Wolfgang Schad "Notes on the Study of Man" in the book *Understanding Children's Drawings* by Michaela Strauss.

2. From the book *At the Gates of Spiritual Science,* a lecture given by Rudolf Steiner. Rudolf Steiner Press, London, 1970.

3. Ibid.

Bibliography

Willi Aeppli, *The Care and Development of the Human Senses*, Rudolf Steiner Schools Fellowship, Forest Row, Sussex 1968.

Amelia Auckett, *Baby Massage*, Hill of Content Publishing Co., Melbourne 1981. Newmarket, New York 1982.

Daisy Bates, *Passing of the Aborigines*, Putnam, London 1938.

Joan Beck, *How to Raise a Brighter Child*, Fontana, London 1973.

Emil Bock, *Genesis*, Floris Books, Edinburgh 1986.

Hilde Boos-Hamburger, *The Creative Power of Colour*, Michael Press, UK 1973.

John Bowlby, *Child Care and the Growth of Love*, Penguin, London 1970.

Walter Braithwaite, *A Book of Songs*, Stourbridge, Worcs 1970.

Kate Campbell and Elizabeth A. Wilmot, *A Guide to the Care of the Young Child*, Department of Health, Victoria, Australia 1972.

Frans Carlgren, *Education Towards Freedom*, Lanthorn Press, East Grinstead, Sussex 1976.

Gudrun Davy and Bons Voors, *Lifeways*. Hawthorn Press, Stroud, UK 1983.

Lore Deggler, *The Dogma of Materialism - an effort in overcoming it in physics*, unpublished paper.

Glen Doman, *Teach Your Baby to Read*, Cape, London 1965.

Stanley Drake, *The Path to Birth*, Floris Books, Edinburgh 1979.

Rudolf Dreikurs, *Happy Children*, Fontana, London 1972.

Arnold Gesell, *How a Baby Grows*, Hamish Hamilton Medical Books, London 1946.

Herbert Ginsberg and Sylvia Opper, *Piaget's Theory of Intellectual Development - an Introduction*, Prentice Hall Inc, New Jersey 1969.

Ursula Grahl, *The Wisdom in Fairy Tales*, New Knowledge Books, East Grinstead 1972.

Jacob Grimm, *The Complete Grimm's Fairy Tales*, Routledge, London 1975.

A. C. Harwood, *The Way of a Child*, Rudolf Steiner Press, London 1967.

Margaretha Hauschka, *Rhythmical Massage*, Rudolf Steiner Press, London 1979.

Rudolf Hauschka, *Nutrition*, Rudolf Steiner Press, London 1983.

Hugh Jolly, *Book of Child Care*, Allen and Unwin, London 1985.

Carl Jung, *Modern Man in Search of a Soul*, Routledge, London 1968.

Archie Kalokerinos, *Every Second Child*, Keats Pub. Inc. 1986.

E. and L. Kolisko, *Agriculture of Tomorrow*, Kolisko Archives, Bournemouth 1978.

Karl König, *Embryology and World Evolution*, translated by R. E. K. Meuss FIL, reprinted from *British Homeopathic Journal*, 1965.

The First Three Years of the Child, Anthroposophic Press, New York 1969.

The Human Soul, Anthroposophic Press, New York 1973.

La Leche League, *The Womanly Art of Breast Feeding*, La Leche League International, Franklin Park, Illinois 1958, 1963, 1981.

Martin Large, *Who's Bringing Them Up?* Hawthorn Press, Stroud 1981.

Elizabeth Lebret, *Pentatonic Songs*, Waldorf Association of Ontario 1978.

Janine Lévy, *Exercises for Your Baby*, translated by Elra Gleasure, Collins, London 1978.

Jean Liedloff, *The Continuum Concept*, Futura Publications Ltd., London 1976.

Astrid Lindgren, *The Tomten*, Viking Kestrel, London 1985.

George MacDonald, *The Princess and the Goblin*, Chariot Books.

Gladys Mayer, *The Mystery Wisdom of Colour*, New Knowledge Books, East Grinstead, Sussex 1975.

Ashley Montagu, *Touching: the Human Significance of the Skin*, Columbia University Press, New York 1971.

Maria Montessori, *The Secret of Childhood*, Jangam Books, London 1983.

Raymond S. and Dorothy N. Moore, *Better Late than Early*, Readers Digest Press, New York 1975.

Richard Moskowitz, *The Case Against Immunisation*, National Centre for Homeopathy, 1500 Massachusetts Avenue NW, Washington DC, 20005.

Jennifer Mulherin, Editor, *Popular Nursery Rhymes*, Granada, London 1981.

Joseph Chilton Pearce, *The Magical Child*, Bantam New Age Books, New York 1980.

Virginia Phillips, *Successful Breast Feeding*, Nursing Mothers' Association of Australia, Melbourne 1976.

Gerhard Schmidt, *The Dynamics of Nutrition*, translated by G. F. Karnow, Biodynamic Literature, Wyoming 1980.

Rupert Sheldrake, *A New Science of Life*, A. Blond, London 1985.

Benjamin Spock, *Baby and Child Care*, 4th Edition, The Bodley Head, London 1979.

Rudolf Steiner, *Agriculture*, Bio-dynamic Agriculture Association, London 1977.

Rudolf Steiner, *At the Gates of Spiritual Science*, Rudolf Steiner Press, London 1970.

Rudolf Steiner, *Colour*, Rudolf Steiner Press. London 1977.

Rudolf Steiner, *Cosmic Memory*, Harper and Row, San Francisco 1981.

Rudolf Steiner, *Human Values in Education*, Anthroposophic Press, New York 1969.

Rudolf Steiner, *Nine Lectures on Bees*, St George Publications, Spring Valley, New York 1975.

Rudolf Steiner, *Occult Science - an Outline*, Rudolf Steiner Press, London 1969.

Rudolf Steiner, *Study of Man*, Rudolf Steiner Press, London 1966.

Rudolf Steiner, *Theosophy*, Rudolf Steiner Press, London 1965.

Rudolf Steiner, *Genesis, The Biblical Story of Creation*, Rudolf Steiner Press, London 1982.

Anne Willis Stonehouse, *A Must, a Maybe or a Mistake - Parents and Toddlers Groups*, The Lady Gowrie Child Centre, Melbourne, Australia 1981.

Michaela Strauss, *Understanding Children's Drawings*, Rudolf Steiner Press, London.

D. W. Winnicott, *The Child, the Family and the Outside World*, Tavistock, London 1964.

Wilhelm Zur Linden, *A Child is Born*, Rudolf Steiner Press, London 1985.

Further Recommended Reading

Heidi Britz-Crecelius, *Children at Play*, Floris Books, Edinburgh 1979.
Diana Carey and Judy Large, *Festivals, Family and Food*. Hawthorn Press, Stroud, UK 1982.
D. Coplen, *Parenting*, Floris Books, Edinburgh 1982.
Francis Edmunds, *Rudolf Steiner's Gift to Education*, Rudolf Steiner Press, London.
Arnold Gesell, *The First Five Years of Life*, Methuen, London 1954.
Maria Geuter, *Herbs in Nutrition*, Bio-Dynamic Agricultural Association, London 1962.
Caroline Von Heydebrand, *Childhood*, Anthroposophical Publishing Co., London 1942.
Marshall H. Klaus and John H. Kennell, *Parent-Infant Bonding*, Mosby, London 1982.
Frederick Le Boyer, *Birth Without Violence*, Wildwood House, London 1975.
Betty Preston, *What Shall I Do Now?* Hodder, London 1968.
Karen Pryor, *Nursing Your Baby*, Harper and Row, New York 1973.
Irma Schnierer, *Parents ask Why*, Angus and Robertson, London 1940.
Rudolf Steiner, *Education of the Child*, Rudolf Steiner Press, London 1985.
Rudolf Steiner, *Festivals and their Meaning*, Rudolf Steiner Press, London 1981.
Rudolf Steiner, *Health and Illness*, Vol. 1, Anthroposophic Press, Spring Valley, New York 1981.
Rudolf Steiner, *Man's Being, his Destiny, and World Evolution*, Anthroposophic Press, New York 1966.
Rudolf Steiner, *Results of Spiritual Investigation*, Garber Communications, New York 1973.
Rudolf Steiner, *The Kingdom of Childhood*, Rudolf Steiner Press, London.
Rudolf Steiner, *The Story of my Life*, Anthroposophic Press, New York 1951.
Marie Winn, *The Plug in Drug*, Bantam Books, New York 1977.
Ruth Wittig, *A Child's Work*, Melbourne Rudolf Steiner School, Australia 1979.

Index

Useful Addresses and Resources

Australia

Nursing Mothers of Australia, Melbourne
Gabriel Baby Centre, 6 Norman Avenue, S. Yarra, Victoria 3141

United Kingdom

La Leche League of Great Britain
BM 3424
London WC1V 6XX
Tel. 01 404 5011

National Childbirth Trust
9 Queensborough Terrace
Bayswater
London W2 3TB

La Leche League Leaflets

- 11 *Managing Nipple Problems*
- 29 *Sore Breast* (plugged duct and infections)
- 80 *Breastfeeding after a Caesarian Birth*
- 167 *The Biological Specificity of Milk*
  (why to feed a baby breast rather than other milk)
- 715 *Crying - Why and What to Do*

Most of books listed below are easily obtainable at bookshops; books marked with an asterisk can only be obtained through the La Leche League at present.

The Womanly Art of Breastfeeding,★ LLL Manual.
Breast is Best, Drs P. & A. Stanway, Pan Books.
The Experience of Breastfeeding, Sheila Kitzinger, Penguin.
How to Really Love Your Child, Dr R. Campbell, Victor Books.
The Family Bed: An Age Old Concept in Child Rearing,★ Tine Thevenin.
Your Child's Self Esteem, D. C. Briggs, Dolphin Books.
Touching, Ashley Montagu, Harper & Row.
New Life, A. & J. Balaskas, Sidgwick & Jackson.
Pregnancy and Childbirth, Sheila Kitzinger, Michael Joseph.
Birth at Home, Sheila Kitzinger, Oxford University Press.
Caesarian Birth,★ The Caesarian Support Group of Cambridge.
  (Their current address is available from LLLGB.)

USA

La Leche League International
9616 Minneapolis Ave
Franklin Park
Illinois 60131

Resources in Human Nurturing, International (RHNI)
3885 Forest Street
PO Box 6861
Denver, Colorado 80206

Peggy O'Mara McMahon
(for breastfeeding an infant with cleft palate)
Star Rte
PO Box 373
Placitas
New Mexico 87043
Tel. 505 867 4391

Mothering
PO Box 8410
Santa Fe
New Mexico 87504
This magazine contains many references, articles and sources of help.

Reducing the risk of cot death

(Additional information compiled by Hawthorn Press)

Very occasionally babies die suddenly for no obvious reason, from what is called 'cot death' or 'sudden infant death syndrome' (SIDS). Although the causes are still unclear, placing a baby to sleep on his or her back reduces the risk, as does ensuring a cigarette smoke-free environment. Another possible contributory factor is overheating.

Below is a comprehensive list of all steps you can take to diminish the risk of cot death:

Sleeping place and position:
- Always put your baby to sleep on his or her back, unless a doctor has advised otherwise for specific reasons.
- Keep your baby's cot in your bedroom for the first six months or so
- Don't use plastic sheets or have ribbons or bits of string (e.g. mobiles) near the cot where your baby can get caught in them.
- Make sure there is no gap between the cot mattress and the side of the cot through which your baby can slip down.
- Make sure the mattress is firm, flat and clean. The outside of the mattress should be waterproof, but not have any loose plastic covering that could come off and choke your baby. Fire-retardant materials found in some cot mattresses are probably best avoided, though no direct link with cot death has been proved.
- Use sheets and lightweight blankets but not duvets, quilts, bedding rolls or pillows etc.
- Don't leave your baby to sleep propped up on a cushion on a sofa, or in an armchair.

Overheating:
- Don't let your baby get too hot and don't overheat the room. If the room is warm enough for you to be comfortable in light clothing, this is the right temperature for your baby too (16-20°C).
- Keep your baby's head uncovered in bed. A baby needs to lose heat from his or her head and face. By placing your baby in the 'feet to foot' position (with his/her feet right at the end of the cot), you prevent the baby wriggling under the covers.

- Remove hats and extra clothing whenever you come indoors or enter a warm place (e.g. a train or car).
- If you take your baby into your bed to sleep, make sure he/she is not too hot under your duvet.
- Never give the baby a hot water bottle or an electric blanket.
- If your baby is feverish, don't give him or her extra bedding.

Smoking:
- Stop smoking in pregnancy. This also applies to fathers! (Babies and young children exposed to cigarette smoke are also more susceptible to coughs, asthma and chest/ear infections.)
- No one should smoke in the same room as your baby.
- If you are a smoker it is possible that sharing your bed with a baby may increase the risk of cot death.

In general, always ask for a doctor's advice quickly if your baby seems at all unwell. Cot death is rare – take the precautions listed above but don't let fear of it spoil the first precious months with your baby.

Other Books from Hawthorn Press

MOTHERING WITH SOUL
Raising children as special work
Joan Salter
Good mothering is important work, yet is undervalued. From her work and conversations with young mothers, Joan Salter explores the profound experiences of intimate sharing, pregnancy, birth and the first years which are unique to mothering. She explores the spiritual, soul and practical work of mothering so that this womanly art is affirmed as a special vocation.
144pp; 210 x 135mm; paperback; 1 869 890 84 1

HELPING CHILDREN TO OVERCOME FEAR
The healing power of play
Russell Evans
Critical illness can cause overwhelming feelings of abandonment and loss. Difficult for adults to face alone, for children the experience is magnified. Jean Evans was a play leader who recognised ahead of her time the importance of enabling children to give voice to their feelings, providing opportunities for play and working in partnership with parents.
128pp; 216 x 138mm; paperback; 1 903458 02 1

STORYTELLING WITH CHILDREN
Nancy Mellon
Telling stories awakens wonder and creates special occasions with children, whether it is bedtime, around the fire or on rainy days. Nancy Mellon shows how you can become a confident storyteller and enrich your family with the power of story.
192pp; 216 x 138mm; illustrations; paperback; 1 903458 08 0

FREE TO LEARN
Introducing Steiner Waldorf early childhood education
Lynne Oldfield
Free to Learn is a unique guide to the principles and methods of Steiner Waldorf early childhood education. This authoritative introduction is written by Lynne Oldfield, Director of the London Steiner Waldorf Early Childhood Teacher Training course. She draws on kindergarten

experience from around the world, with stories, helpful insights, lively observations and pictures. This inspiring book will interest parents, educators and early years students. It is up to date, comprehensive, includes many photos and has a 16 page colour section.

256pp; 216 x 138mm; colour photographs; paperback; 1 903458 06 4

THE GENIUS OF PLAY
Celebrating the spirit of childhood
Sally Jenkinson

Children move like quick fire from the fantastic to the everyday, when free to express the genius of play. *The Genius of Play* addresses what play is, why it matters, and how modern life endangers children's play. The secrets of play are explored from moving stories and research. Here is an outspoken Children's Play Charter for parents and teachers, which celebrates the playful spirit of childhood.

224pp; 216 x 138mm; colour photographs; paperback; 1 903458 04 8

READY TO LEARN
From birth to school readiness
Martyn Rawson and Michael Rose

When are children ready for school? Many parents are concerned about 'hot housing' their children, about 'too much formal schooling too soon'. *Ready to Learn* will help you consider the transition from kindergarten to school. Here are vivid accounts of child growth, development of the senses, play, discussions about the differences between boys and girls and the right time to introduce reading.

128pp; 216 x 138mm; paperback; 1 903458 15 3

Getting in touch with Hawthorn Press

What are your pressing questions about Lifeways?
The Hawthorn Lifeways Series arises from parents' and educators' pressing questions and concerns – so please contact us with your questions. These will help spark new books and workshops if there is sufficient interest. We will be delighted to hear your views on our Education books, how they can be improved, and what your needs are. Visit our website for details of the Lifeways Series and forthcoming books and events:

http://www.hawthornpress.com

Ordering books

If you have difficulties ordering Hawthorn Press books from a bookshop, you can order direct from:

United Kingdom
Booksource Distribution,
137 Dundee Street, Edinburgh, EH11 1BG
Tel: 0131 229 6800 Fax: 0131 229 9070

North America
Anthroposophic Press c/o Books International,
PO Box 960, Herndon, VA 201 72-0960.
Toll free order line: 800-856-8664
Toll free fax line: 800-277-9747